# THE ULTIMATE GUIDE TO SELF-HEALING TECHNIQUES

Keep Smiling

Love always
Hemali
Chpt. 10

www.hemalivora.com

# THE ULTIMATE GUIDE TO SELF-HEALING TECHNIQUES

25 Home Practices & Tools for Peak Holistic Health & Wellness

LAURA DI FRANCO

**Featuring**: Izabela Adamus, Dr. Shelley Astrof, Barbara M. Bustard, Lori Calvo, Sharon Carne, Bonnie Chase, Dr. Joyce Fishel, Jacqueline M. Kane, Lisa Karasek, Dr. Alice Langholt, M'elle Pirri-Lee, Laura Knapp Mazzotta, Carolyn McGee, Shellie Mekash, Ian Morris, Gerise M. Pappas, Dr. Erika L. Putnam, Nikki Richman, Manuela Rohr, Raelin Saindon, Tina Serocke, Dr. Stacy Snow, Karen Tasto, Hemali V. Vora

Brave Healer Productions

The Ultimate Guide to Self-Healing Techniques
25 Home Practices & Tools for Peak Holistic Health and Wellness

Laura Di Franco, MPT


ISBN (paperback): 978-1-7330738-8-2
ISBN (ebook): 978-1-7330738-9-9

# Dedication

To the women of my Intuitive Writing and Speaking for Healer Entrepreneurs course: Holy moly goddesses, you continue to floor me with your badassery. Thank you so much for stepping up to the plate and sharing your gifts out loud with the world; a world that sorely needs us right now. You all light my fire and have been my true inspiration for the programs I've created these past four years. This book is an incredibly powerful collaboration and exactly the energy the Brave Healer Revolution was founded with! Thank you for being a part of that from the beginning, for trusting me to guide you, and maybe sometimes drag you a little, down this path. I'm so honored to be walking along side you on this journey!

# Contents

**Introduction** 1

**Chapter 1:** Consciousness 7
The Key to Healing
*by Lisa Karasek, Quantum Healer*

**Chapter 2:** Journaling 15
Using Writing as a Healing Tool
*by Laura Di Franco, MPT*

**Chapter 3:** Intuition 101 22
How to Connect to Your Inner Guide
*by Tina Serocke, MOT, OTR/L*

**Chapter 4:** Showing Up 31
A Tool for Self-Acceptance and Love
*by Lori Calvo, MHSA, NBC-HWC*

**Chapter 5:** Awakening Intuition 39
The Key to Success with Reiki
*by Dr. Alice Langholt, Ph.D.*

**Chapter 6:** Simple Meditation 45
Quiet the Mind and Heal the Body
*by Dr. Shelley Astrof, M.Ed., D. Meditation*

**Chapter 7:** Grounding and Centering 53
Clarity Through Heart Connection
*by Carolyn McGee, CLC, MNST, CRM, EFT*

**Chapter 8:** Self Awareness 62
Reduce Stress with the Enneagram
*by Gerise M. Pappas, CPC*

**Chapter 9:** Guided Imagery 71
Using Visualization to Heal
*by Dr. Joyce Fishel, PT, DPT*

**Chapter 10:** Mindful Eating 78
Using Food as Medicine
*by Hemali Vora, MPT, JFB MFR Practitioner*

**Chapter 11:** Tapping 87
Easing Difficult Emotions
*by Laura Knapp Mazzotta, LCSW-R*

**Chapter 12:** Body Awareness 95
Healing Through Somatic Experience
*by Raelin Saindon, B.S. Psy, RMT, C.Ht.*

**Chapter 13:** Breathwork 103
Breathe Your Way to Vitality
*by Karen Tasto, CPC, E-RYT*

**Chapter 14:** Acupressure 111
The Points are the Key to Feeling Better
*by Nikki Richman, M.Ac, L.Ac*

**Chapter 15:** Trigger Point Release 119
Resolving Muscular Pain
*by Dr. Stacy Snow, PT, DPT*

**Chapter 16:** Self-Spinal Mobilization 128
Mobilization for Pain Relief & Strong Posture
*by Erika L. Putnam, DC, RYT-500*

**Chapter 17:** Myofascial Release 135
The Wisdom of the Fascia
*by Izabela Adamus, PT*
*Shellie Mekash, CMT*
*M'elle Pirri-Lee, PT*

**Chapter 18:** Yoga 157
Moves for Mindful Pain and Stress Relief
*by Manuela Rohr, BDY/EY, C-IYAT, PRYT*

**Chapter 19:** Total Motion Release 167
Corrective Movement for Pain Relief and Prevention
*by Laura Di Franco, MPT*

**Chapter 20:** Toning 173
The Magic in Your Voice
*by Sharon Carne*

**Chapter 21:** Sound Healing 182
Healing with Frequency Minded Music
*by Ian Morris*

**Chapter 22:** Essential Oils 191
Shift Your Mood & Energy with Scent
*by Bonnie Chase, RN*

**Chapter 23:** Guided Art Therapy 199
The Clay Meditation Ball
*by Barbara M. Bustard*

**Chapter 24:** Energy Healing 205
Clearing Ancestral Energy for Pain Free Living
*by Jacqueline M. Kane*

**Chapter 25:** When to Hire a Guide 214
Take Your Health and Wellness to the Next Level
*by Laura Di Franco, MPT*

# Introduction

True healers teach their clients how to heal themselves instead of only trying to fix them. When we empower others to connect to their healing wisdom, intuition, power, and energy, we heal the world. The mission of this book is to give you the gift of that connection; to teach you powerful self-awareness, healing, and treatment tools you can use at home to nourish your mind, body, and soul and move toward peak holistic health and wellness in every area of your life.

The experts gathered here have trained in their modality, have extensively practiced it on themselves and with countless clients, and have had incredible results teaching these tools. No one tool is cool for every person. So take what resonates and try that. And if it doesn't work, try something else! Remember, many of these tools are a practice. Don't give up after one try. Or even three!

When I began my healing journey as a holistic physical therapist, I quickly saw the need to teach my clients techniques and exercises they could do at home. I wanted to speed up their healing and enhance what we did together in our sessions but also empower them to take responsibility for their healing. When I gave my clients these powerful tools, they'd come back excited, hopeful, and motivated to do just that. That felt purposeful to me. It felt like exactly why I signed up to be a healer. It was awesome when I was able to take someone's pain away in a session, but when I taught them to do that for themselves, I felt a greater sense of accomplishment and purpose.

Over three decades of practice, I've learned, practiced, and taught a lot of tools, really excellent, powerful, profound healing tools. The one idea I could never get on board with was when an instructor preached that his or her modality was the only one and that we should be "purists" in that area of expertise.

One thing I know for sure is there as many ways to heal as there are people on the planet. Each person needs a unique blend or combination of tools. And it's up to us to guide them in terms of what's available and what's possible, to instill hope when someone feels lost. That's why you'll find twenty-five tools in this book. Most of the expert authors will talk about integrating several tools at once, which is one of the beautiful benefits of holistic healing practitioners and what they're here to help you do.

Part of my journey has included John F. Barnes Myofascial Release (JFBMFR), a powerful mind, body, soul healing modality. The most important thing John teaches is how to help our clients with their healing and how to teach the MFR principles. I'm grateful to the three JFBMFR experts who said yes to helping me with that part of this book. You're getting some extra-special guidance with this particular holistic modality because it's been so incredibly powerful in my life and the lives of so many of my clients, friends, family, and colleagues.

What the book starts with, though, is a foundational principle and practice, that if you master it, will significantly enhance everything that follows. Chapter one, written by my very talented healer friend Lisa Karasek, will help you understand awareness and consciousness, the very things that make any modality work. Read slowly through this first chapter as if you were savoring a meal, bite by bite. Taste each bite fully and take notes on what you notice. Come back to this first chapter when another is feeling confusing. Your practice of conscious presence will be the key to mastering all self-healing.

I'm excited to introduce these tools to you. And whether you've dabbled a bit with them already or not, read with a beginner's mind. Ask yourself, what else is possible in terms of my healing today? The authors haven't only shared their tools with you, they've shared themselves, their stories, their passions, and their precious energy with you here on these pages. Soak up every morsel and explore the resources they've shared.

Your incredible healing journey begins now!

# DISCLAIMER

This book offers health and nutritional information and is designed for educational purposes only. You should not rely on this information as a substitute for, nor does it replace professional medical advice, diagnosis, or treatment. If you have any concerns or questions about your health, you should always consult with a physician or other healthcare professional. Do not disregard, avoid, or delay obtaining medical or health-related advice from your healthcare professional because of something you may have read here. The use of any information provided in this book is solely at your own risk.

Developments in medical research may impact the health, fitness, and nutritional advice that appears here. No assurances can be given that the information contained in this book will always include the most relevant findings or developments with respect to the particular material.

Having said all that, know that the experts here have shared their tools, practices, and knowledge with you with a sincere and generous intent to assist you on your health and wellness journey. Please contact them with any questions you may have about the techniques or information they provided. They will be happy to assist you further!

Discipline the mind, the body will follow.
Grand Master John L. Holloway

# Note to the reader

When my Tae Kwon Do Master introduced me to this idea, I was practicing awareness, but not with the passion and intention I do today. Over the last decade, I've come to know the truth of his statement. And so, I offer the chapters in this book in a sort of "order" for you. The chapters that are more mindset-oriented are up front. The chapters that are more physical or body-oriented are next. And the chapters that are somewhere in-between come after that, mostly because if I'd spent too much more time trying to figure out the "right" way to do it, you would have never been reading these pages.

The book can be read in order, or you can pick a chapter to read and practice. You'll be guided several times throughout this book to follow your intuition when it comes to making choices, and you can start right now! Are you drawn to reading it from beginning to end? Or does reading the table of contents and picking a chapter feel like the way to go? There's no wrong way to do it!

Lastly, consider having a notebook or journal handy while you read. Many of the chapters will encourage this. You can download a free one at https://lauradifranco.com/brave-book-resources/.

Enjoy the journey!

CHAPTER 1

# Consciousness

## The Key to Healing

BY LISA KARASEK, QUANTUM HEALER

You're standing in a big, perfect room. You're holding a glass, and then, the glass slips from your hand and crashes to the floor. Large and small pieces of glass go everywhere. Shards of glass spew out, and you're left standing there, saying, *What happened? Why me?*

*Why me* was the question that started it all. I must have said it a thousand times, and at every turn. I still believed everything happened to me. I wasn't yet of the consciousness of what my reality could be. That fact that things were happening to me all the time made me unhappy, and I was ready to feel happy. I wanted a different reality of things not happening *to* me, but *for* me. I was ready to mend my broken glass.

The first thing I did was get curious. What were those things that were always happening to me? And why? I questioned everything, including the questions. I learned that of all those things happening to me was my broken glass on the floor; my truth, my soul, broken and fragmented, and all over the place.

I began picking the pieces up, one by one, and started looking at them more closely than I had ever looked at anything in my entire life. At first, it was very elementary, superficial stuff, like when I felt the need to defend myself because someone misrepresented my truth. It made me feel like they were telling lies about me, making me out to be someone I'm not. What I was doing was acknowledging the cause and effect of things. And the more curious I got, the more I began to see what my chunks of glass were made of.

The big chunks were feelings like being betrayed and unworthiness. I had the hardest time figuring out why I always felt invisible and why I wasn't being seen for who I am or what I'm capable of. It wasn't so much who made me feel this way, but why I felt this way. They were belief systems that I was operating from, but they didn't actually belong to me. They were learned behaviors that I had to overcome, and I am continuing to overcome them.

The smaller pieces of glass represent the emotions and the reactions I have attached to the wounds that I have developed from the traumas I experienced or witnessed; of hardship, isolation, and degradation. Like why me? These are the feelings I've had to heal, and what I continue to be mindful of.

The shards were all of the events, circumstances, and experiences I've suffered through, that broke me down and left me full of anger, resentment, and frustration. They are all those arguments (real and imagined), the abuse and torment I endured, and everything that ever made me cry. The shards cut in deep and caused me to harden my heart, build walls, and protect myself. Now, as I collect and re-story them, it's easier to move past them.

*Consciousness is to ask yourself—what are my pieces of broken glass?*

I began to think about every time I sacrificed myself. All the times I allowed my father to convince me and everyone that I didn't know what I was doing, that I didn't know anything. I thought about every time I compromised myself and for whom, like saying yes when I really wanted to say no, and the times it was just easier to agree. It was becoming evident that I was giving pieces of myself away every time.

When we do this we give away our truth, our essence, and pieces of our soul. We allow ourselves to be distanced from our true selves, our purpose, and our sincere intentions. Every time we allow someone else's energy or belief to infiltrate or distort ours, we're letting our consciousness project away from us. We're dropping our glass on the floor.

You picked up this book because you're ready to pick up your pieces.

## Step one is getting curious.

Something changed how you perceive your reality, and you question it. And once you learn something, you're different. I'm presuming based on what you know now, you want to feel differently. You're ready to feel good. Like me, you want to be sure to clean up all those shards and pieces, big and small, meticulously, so you don't get hurt again.

## Step two is deciding what to do next.

*Consciousness is grounding a non-physical idea into a physical reality.*

It's time to take action, but before you do, you have to muster up the courage and the bravery needed to do it. This is when you begin practicing awareness, presence, and mindfulness, whether you realize that's what you're doing or not. These all help you with courage and bravery because you begin to see your pieces more clearly. You begin creating your practices and setting your intentions from this new perspective and clarity. And those lead to creating a new sense of reality, the reality you desire to have for your self.

## What's next?

You practice what you want your reality to be.

You're picking up the pieces one by one, and one by one they begin to shine in the light from the window you're holding them up to. They're you, by the way, if you missed it.

Your new practice is providing a much-needed sense of confidence and stability. And you're probably beginning to say to yourself at this point, "*I got this.*" Little by little, you're beginning to feel on your way to being whole.

Some actions you may want to consider at this point if you aren't already doing so are things like taking classes, finding a mentor, and securing that one special person that you feel closest to and who you trust. You're ready to go a little deeper.

And even with all of these, there's still more to do. The tool that I started with, what truly started giving me the most insight and clarity, was Grounding.

Grounding is one of those things that seems like an easy one, but it is a bit more involved than you might think. Remember, you're working on a perceived ideal and turning it into your reality. You want to ground yourself into your intentions and make sure they stick.

Don't sweat it, though. Once you get the hang of it, you will come to appreciate all that it offers and honor grounding for its value. You'll begin to see how it's the most integral part of this process and the essential tool, before diving into all the others.

Grounding is not the step you want to skimp on. It's an essential practice in its own right, and for good reason. Grounding sets you up for the successful and sustainable completion of everything that follows it.

Grounding is about your sincerity. Without sincerity, your intentions won't mean much, not to you or anyone else. Sincerity equals value. If your real intention is to change (i.e. heal), your purpose has to have worth. It's worth it to heal yourself. I can't think of any reason why anyone wouldn't want to be serious when it comes to healing.

Please, learn a few grounding exercises. Try them out. You have to find what works for you and what feels right to do. No rule says you can only do one thing. They each provide something different, and there's a place and time for everything, just like every tool in this book. You're not purchasing this book for only one chapter; your plan is to learn every tool. It's good to have a full toolbox.

I have at least five different grounding exercises that I use all the time, but I want to share with you now what my favorite grounding exercise is.

Let's begin together.

1. Dress comfortably and find a space where you can stand without any distractions. If standing isn't your thing, then sit comfortably, and uncross your knees and ankles. Have your feet flat on the floor.

2. Stand with your feet hip-width apart, and soften your knees. When you lock your knees, you block the energy flow! Grounding is very much an energetic process, and you want to practice good habits.

3. Gently shift your weight to your right side, and begin to slowly roll your feet to the right side. You're stretching your ankles so that you are now standing on the outer edge of your right foot, and the arch of your left foot. You should be standing as straight as you can (if you're not there yet, you will be. Keep practicing). Keep your knees soft. Your body will never ask for pain, so check in to make sure there's no pressure at your knees or ankles. If so, adjust yourself. Find the right spot that works for you. Every body is different.

4. Take a few mindful, slow breaths, and pause here.

5. Now, gently shift your weight to your left side, and stretch your ankles until you have rolled your feet to the other side. Allow the soles of your feet to come into full contact with the floor as you roll from your right to the left side. Imagine there are four corners to each of your soles and have each corner touch down through the roll. It's a very soft and fluid motion. Now you should be standing on the outer edge of your left foot, and the arch of your right foot. Stand up straight (but with soft knees), and keep your spine as tall as possible, keeping a good flow of energy. You're also creating both physical and mental balancing.

6. Take a few mindful, slow breaths as you pause here.

7. Shift and roll to your right side again. Remember to be mindful of your posture and have all four corners touch down through the roll. Make adjustments if necessary so that you aren't toppling over. Keep your knees soft.

8. Take a few mindful, slow breaths as you pause here.

9. Shift and roll to your left side again. Are you feeling it yet?

10. Now, you may begin to gently rock yourself back and forth very slowly, and in pace with your breath. Easy goes it. Keep your flow of energy steady and comfortable. If you find it helpful, find a focal point to concentrate on somewhere in front of you. Hold onto a chair back or other object that is of the right height for your stability. If sitting, allow your body to go with the flow.

You only need to do this for as little or as much as you need to. Some people like to set a timer for 2 or 3 minutes, or you can just stop when you feel ready. Your nervous system is being activated, and you should feel your whole body relax. Rock until you feel appropriately relaxed.

11. Shake it off! Your nervous system was activated, and your body found points of tension in this exercise, so give your arms a quick wave or 3 above your head, and a few friendly low kicks in front of you, and a little wiggle in the middle for fun. This releases any tension and pulls your energy into you.

Once you get the hang of this grounding exercise, you can do it anywhere, any time. You can do it in front of people, and they won't know what you're doing or why. Can you feel why this one is my favorite?

To watch a full video demonstration on this technique, please go to my resources page: www.LisaKarasek.com/resources

I practice multiple grounding techniques, and each one has its own purpose and intention. These are my go-to's:

- Shower with the intention to ground
- Create sacred space
- Speak to your angels and spirit guides
- Routines and rituals

About those big and little pieces of glass (also known as *Shadows*), the more you work on them, the less distorted your glass will look once it's all mended back together.

Give yourself space and time. Everything is a process, and you will find that each piece of glass that gets picked up and returned to you as healed, the more you grow and develop. What you learn as you retrieve the pieces of your soul is a journey, and it can be as easy or as difficult as you make it out to be. It all requires the same amount of energy, so why not go for the good stuff?

In time it will all begin to pay off, and you will start to see the building of your reality, and begin to feel all that has transcended, and you will begin to sense what still needs to be realized.

Continue to find and sweep up the shards, and you will once again hold in your hand a sturdy glass. The glass is you, by the way, if you missed it.

That glass is full of choices. What you're doing with them is becoming; becoming your process, without having to break it down.

---

**Lisa Karasek is an expert Quantum Healer and Intuitive Practitioner. She is a TRE® Certified Facilitator and Certified Eating Psychology Coach, who is able to update her client's states of being to assist in healing. Using ancient, multi-dimensional healing, and Holistic Metamorphosis® (an angelic energy modality), Consciousness-based practices, and TRE® (tension and trauma releasing exercises), Lisa powerfully guides her clients to a healthier, happier, more purposeful life. Lisa is dedicated and passionate about helping you work with the dynamics of your self-relationship and believes this is the key to most Mind Body Spirit disease and illness.**

**Integrating energetic and spiritual transformation through Mind Body Spirit Guidance. Because everyone deserves an authentic self relationship.**

**Find more information about working with Lisa and her programs please visit www.LisaKarasek.com**
**Resources page: www.LisaKarasek.com/resources**

CHAPTER 2

# Journaling

## Using Writing as a Healing Tool

BY LAURA DI FRANCO, MPT

### My story

When I was fifteen, I started writing in a little blue diary with one of those tiny silver locks. It was about five inches wide and six inches tall, and it hid well in my purse. I wrote poems and musings, mostly about boys and heartache, and why the world was unfair, and what I'd be when I grew up. I freely and regularly unloaded my soul onto those pages. And I healed there a little bit with every word, feeling, idea, or story, whether I knew that was happening at the time or not.

I was a year away from driving and knew everything. I was a high school soccer star, had my first real boyfriend, ended my virginity that year, got my first work permit, and was out of my house every chance I got. There was a lot of thinking, pondering, dreaming, crying, question-asking, and growing going on. The writing felt like a refuge many days, a secret place where I could be me, and nobody could say anything about that. It was a place I could break the rules without anyone knowing, and say the things I couldn't speak out loud. I told my story on those pages, to myself.

Today they call this narrative therapy. Therapeutic journaling is something you can even get certified to teach now. Psychologists talk about the power of writing your story and how giving a witness to your childhood, and not-so-childhood traumas and tragedies can help you heal.

What I know is that writing has always been the way I Feng Shui'd my soul to clear a space inside me by moving the energy. I'd write and move my pain from inside to outside onto the paper. When it was out loud like that, it was real. I realize now that I was clearing a space for a deeper connection and creative flow to move through me. I was helping clear the clutter and the noise drowning out my intuition.

The more years that went by and the more healing I did in all forms, the more my writing became a channel for my purpose, and a bigger voice to move through. I wrote my way through my life, my marriage, the births of my two children, my career choices, traumas, death of loved ones, a move across the country, adventures, and vacations, my divorce, and a six-year journey my son and I took ending in earning our black belts in Tae Kwon Do together.

*OMG, that's it,* I thought one morning. *This is my book!* It was 2012, and my son and I were one test away from earning our black belts. In six years of journals, I'd detailed every step of the martial arts journey with my son, including how it was feeling to be a wife, mother, healer, and practicer of a combat sport in my late thirties. Those six, eight-by-eleven-inch journals became my very first book, an inspirational memoir called *Living, Healing, and Tae Kwon Do.* Writing that book was massive healing for my self worth and kicking that pebble would be starting an avalanche in terms of using writing to teach others another tool for their healing.

Not everyone will write books from their journals. Even those who know they have a book in them may need to do a more free-form version of writing before they get to the book writing. I realized this very thing in 2015 when I thought I had my second book moving through me. A friend dropped an email in my inbox about

NaNoWriMo (National Novel Writing Month), and after reading about the 30-day program, I was stoked. *This is just what I need to finish this book*, I thought. The goal of the program that November was to write a thirty-thousand-word novel in thirty days.

At the end of that thirty-day program, I had a sixty-five-thousand word book written that detailed every wound of my childhood. I attached it to an email and sent it to my family on Christmas Eve of that same year. The good news? My family still talks to me. The point? That book would not be the book anyone would read. It was the Feng Shui that needed to happen to clear a space for the real book to be born. I had to give myself permission to write freely, without censoring myself. I had to allow myself to write until I was empty, until my soul felt satisfied and healed, and until the story was told in its entirety. I prioritized my healing when I chose to write those words. And every time I write or publish nowadays, I do the same thing.

"You own everything that happened to you.
Tell your stories. If they wanted you to write warmly
about them, they should've behaved better."
Anne Lamott

You may also have books-worth of words inside you that need to be expressed. When you journal don't attach to the writing being any particular thing. Write for you and you only. If you're worried about others reading your stuff, then burn the pages afterward. It's more about the shifting of energy than it is about anything else. The writing moves and shifts the energy. The healing process happens when you shift the energy.

Writing also might surprise you. You may connect with memories, thoughts, ideas, or feelings that you didn't know were there. One day I looked down at the pages I was writing on and thought, *do I believe that?* Writing is a powerful self-awareness tool. It helps you feel. And feeling is healing.

The best thing about using writing as a healing tool is that pretty much anyone can do it. If you can't physically write or type for some reason, then record your voice instead because it's the expression of the words that's the key, the shifting of the energy. I'm going to couple the writing with a body awareness meditation to teach you this tool. I call this kind of writing Brave Healing. And it's time to practice. Download a free digital journal at https://lauradifranco.com/brave-book-resources/.

## The tool

**What you'll need:** A notebook, timer, pen, and a space without distractions. If you can't physically write, then record your words with a voice recorder.

**What to keep in mind:** When you do the writing, don't censor yourself. Write as fast as you can without worrying about spelling, punctuation, or grammar.

**Exercise:** You'll find an audio version of the body awareness meditation written below at https://lauradifranco.com/brave-book-resources/.

Find a quiet place where you will not be interrupted and get into a comfortable seated position. Have your notebook and pen handy next to you. Close your eyes, and begin connecting with your body and the breath. Relax and release the head, neck, jaw, and shoulders as you breathe. Soften on each exhale. Relax and release the chest, upper back, and torso. Soften more on each exhale. Relax and release the belly, low back, hips, and butt. Soften a little more with every exhale. Finally, relax down the legs to the feet and continue to soften and let go with every exhale.

As you relax, clear your mind, and connect with the sensations of your body and the environment around you. What do you notice? What do you feel? What do you sense? With every deep inhalation and exhalation, unclench and relax your muscles. Drop your awareness and energy down into your body and just relax there and notice. Spend several minutes in this body awareness meditation, continuing to relax with every exhale.

Open your eyes and set your timer for five minutes. Start writing and fill in the blank: I feel ____. Don't censor yourself. Write as fast as you can until the timer goes off.

This kind of free, automatic, or intuitive writing is a way to connect to your inner guide, healer, and wisdom. Sometimes you'll have way more than five minutes' worth of words. Honor that and write until you feel done. Some days the five-minute prompt will be just what you needed for a quick exercise.

Many people enjoy using writing prompts, including questions, statements, fill-in-the-blanks, and photos to help them get into the flow of the writing. I find that even just a few deep breaths and connecting to the sensations of the body will get you into the flow. Whatever works for you, use it! You can grab my Big Questions ebook of 25 of my favorite writing prompts for free at https://lauradifranco.com/brave-book-resources/.

And one last thing about using writing as a healing tool. There's a connection between handwriting and the brain. You might Google that when you have a moment, but if you're ready to believe me about that science and take a crack at it, you'll find you may feel what the scientists already know; there's a therapeutic reason to write your heart out. Even though I didn't know it back when I was a teen, sitting on my twin bed with my Wonder Woman posters and Shawn Cassidy satin jacket, scribbling my hormone-laden heart and soul onto the tiny white pages of that little blue diary, the blank page was a place to do the sometimes impossible work of healing. And for some reason, that blank slate gave me permission. It made that work a little easier. It provided a safe space, and a different one, to be me.

Now for you, amazing reader, grab one of those extra spiral notebooks you stocked up on from Staples, or that pretty leather thing someone gifted you last year, or just a few sheets of computer paper, and your favorite pen. Take a few deep breaths. You can't get that part wrong. And see what comes when you allow yourself to tell your stories, dream your dreams, vent your woes, explain your wounds, explore your soul, and meet your true self on the page. Ask yourself, what else is possible for my healing today?

One of the reasons I put the journaling chapter up front here is that I highly suggest you keep a journal as you explore the rest of the healing tools in this book. Journaling will be a perfect adjunct to any other healing tool you practice and a place where you can keep track of what you felt, note down things you want to remember, list ideas that come to you, note Aha moments, and keep track of your progress as you move through the book and the tools. I have many different notebooks for different purposes and love to organize that way. You might keep one notebook for your favorite quotes, another for a course you're working on, and yet another for straight-up daily journal entries. I've kept one for blog and book title ideas, and another for budget and finance notes. Be creative with your notebook badassery y'all.

Now onto chapter three, where my friend Tina helps you connect with your intuition. Your journal will be a fantastic place to take notes about that as you learn those powerful tools. I can't wait to hear how these tools are working for you! Please come on over to www.BraveHealer.com and fill out the contact form. Tell me about your experiences and ask your questions!

---

**Laura Di Franco, MPT, is the owner of Brave Healer Productions, where she'll help you share your story, build your business and change the world. With three decades of expertise in holistic physical therapy, a third-degree black belt, and ten books, she has a clear preference for being badass, but she's also the champion of entrepreneurs who want to grow their health-based practices to the next level. Her writing workshops, business strategy sessions, and online writing club are just some of the ways she helps talented professionals maximize their professional impact.**

**Laura's a mom of two amazing kids, an inspirational speaker, international blogger, certified content marketer, and content coordinator for Potomac Living and Bethesda Living Magazines. She's also a spoken-word poet with a passion for words that heal. You'll often find her at local open mic nights with her poet-loving friends, sipping a mojito.**

**If she's not writing or speaking, you'll most likely find her driving her convertible Mustang, eating dark chocolate, or bouncing to the beat at a rave. She runs her private practice, Bodyworks Physical Therapy, in Bethesda, Maryland, where she lives with her two dogs, Reina and Leo. www.BraveHealer.com**

CHAPTER 3

# Intuition 101

## How to Connect to Your Inner Guide

BY TINA SEROCKE, MOT, OTR/L

## My Story

As early as the tender age of five, I would awaken at 5:00 a.m. without an alarm clock, and find myself walking to the dark and eerily-quiet living room to lie on our velvety sofa and curl up with my mom's hand-stitched afghan. My parents and sister were still fast asleep in their respective beds. I would sink into the softness and curl up in the fetal position and wait for "The time that was to come" consistently occurring at 5:55 a.m. every single weekday. Every weekday at 5:00 a.m. Waiting patiently. *Would it happen again today?* I'd often think.

Those 55 minutes of solitude were peaceful, relaxing bliss. Then without fail, I would awaken fully at 5:55 a.m. and look to the kitchen door. The glorious morning sunshine would fill the kitchen with the warmth of yellow and orange hues. Just like clockwork, I would hear a key turn in the old lock of the back door in the kitchen. The knob would make a metallic, turning sound, and then the heavy wooden door would be pushed open, squeaking until it stopped. With the bright sunshine illuminating the room, I would clearly see the silhouette of a tall man, over six feet, wearing a suit and top hat as he entered the doorway with five, loud, heavy footsteps. As his shoes shuffled across the old wooden floorboards, they squeaked beneath his stride. He turned, and as he closed the door, it creaked on the well-worn hinges, and I would hear the clicking of the metal as the door latched.

*Who the hell is that man? Could anyone else hear or see this? Am I awake, or am I dreaming?* I would ask myself this, time and time again. I vividly recall asking my mom if she heard the door squeak in the mornings, and she shook her head no, and adamantly said, "No, the back door is always locked." Indeed it was, yet this silhouetted-man, unlocked that door every weekday like clockwork. The realization came from deep within me; this was a gift I was experiencing. Gifts of wisdom from a higher source. That 55 minutes I spent on the sofa in solitude five days a week was spent in an altered state. Not awake and not asleep. I came to realize I was receiving spiritual downloads. It was a time of moving inward for personal reflection, and an invitation to "hear and see," which gave me insight as to what lie ahead for me.

This spirit, a guide, knew I was there. I could tell by his glance at me. And I intuitively knew I was safe. We tend to fear entities or spirits because there is a "dark" association. The darkness you fear is powerless. Our societal belief systems are what created the fear of other-worldly beings or spirit. They're here to convey messages. I trusted myself to know in my gut that I was safe from harm during the 55 minutes I was on the sofa, waiting. I felt strong currents of subtle energy flowing through my body on both physical and spiritual levels, which opened up channels to flow with vibration. The beauty of this subtle energy, which can be intense and overbearing or flowing and gentle, can be used to warn us of good and bad things. As an awakened person, this subtle energy can warn us and protect us from harm. The feelings in the body may be felt as tingling or buzzing as the energy flows. This is my earliest memory of receiving guidance and the beginning of my journey of spiritual awakening.

## Later years: Listening to intuition or gut

One morning at around 2:00 a.m., I was driving home alone after an evening spent with friends. It was an easy, albeit dark, drive home. No moon to guide me. After exiting the highway, I was waiting at a stoplight, and my body began to shake from deep inside my core. Yet, I continued along the road, ignoring the shaking in my body. Something was wrong. Terribly wrong. A warning sign to heed. Yes, I ignored it.

I turned left onto the four-lane road that passed through a wildlife preserve and continued into the far-right lane. Suddenly, I felt a tremendous sense of urgency to move into the left lane. My body was under attack with pressure from all sides, squeezing my ribcage, taking my breath away. *Damn it; I don't want to move. Leave me alone!* I thought. Then, it happened. The hard, cold slap to my right cheek burned my face. *Seriously? What-The-&@$%?* After a split second of feeling the burn, a second slap assaulted me! Now I was angry. Really angry. I screamed out loud, "Fine!" Emphatically, "Fine!"

I swiftly veered into the left lane with seconds to spare, and abruptly came across a gathering of five deer standing in the right lane of the road, directly in my previous path! Their eyes illuminated green, as my headlights lit up their figures in the roadway. As my foot hit the brakes, my body lurched forward in my car seat. Coming to a slow roll, I began searching desperately for signs of deer lurking elsewhere in the last quarter mile of the wildlife preserve. I gasped for air as my lungs were tight and suffocating. My aching muscles were balled up, and I realized I was gripping the steering wheel for dear life. *Wow!* The realization finally hit. *I. Am. Alive. Unharmed.* I realized the profound importance of listening to my gut feelings. I felt sincere gratitude for the guidance that I received to change lanes. When I didn't want to listen to the guidance, my gut kicked in and slapped me to get my attention. Because I listened, finally, I avoided what would have likely been a major, life-altering accident.

Operating on autopilot leads one astray from living a purposeful life. There is nothing to fear from listening to our gut feelings, as this is an inner wisdom that comes from our higher power, higher self, or soul. All we need to do is listen and watch for the signs. They are everywhere. More on this later.

## The Tool

Listening to your gut feeling is not only essential, but it can also be considered your moral compass. Many of us have forgotten how to listen to our gut instincts. When we were younger, listening to our intuition came naturally. We laughed when happy, screamed when angry or hurt, cried when sad, became frozen or frantic when struck with fear, and danced and jiggled around when elated. This all came naturally to us. No brainpower was involved. The problem is that as we matured, most of us changed under societal pressures and began listening to our heads instead of our bodies, as nature intended.

Have you ever tried to push through a decision thinking it was necessary just to do it?

Have you ever wanted to zig when your pit-of-the-stomach feeling tells you to zag?

Have that gut feeling that if you push through with a decision or action that big problems may be the result? Being in that fear is being afraid of your intuition.

Your intuition is that part of you that knows what is best deep down inside, even when your brain can't explain it and wants to override it. It may be other people's opinions or your expectations that point you in a specific direction. Yet if you choose to follow your gut, and connect with your intuitive nature, a self-awareness begins to emerge.

Everything you feel, think, and do are your lessons in this life, on this physical plane. Societal pressures and belief systems you have been taught are the real challenges! Connecting with your intuition will allow an authentic spiritual connection to self on your journey.

Let's take a look at how you connect deeper with your intuition. If you spend your life always listening to your head, instead of your gut, you are not grounded or centered. Below are some exercises that will help you to get centered and thus tune into your intuition. The more often we do this, the easier it becomes.

If you would like to listen to an audio version of the exercise written below, you'll find it here https://intuitivebodytherapeutics.com/resources/

## Grounding Exercise

This grounding exercise can be visualized at any time and will deepen your intuitive abilities. Optimally you'd want to be in nature, sinking your bare feet into the sand or grass, near an ocean or lake to experience a powerful grounding connection. If there's inclement weather, this can be conducted indoors, in a quiet area, seated, or lying down.

If you can be outside, find a serene area to do this exercise and slip off your shoes, letting your bare feet feel the ground. Take a few moments to allow yourself time to feel your feet completely connecting to the earth, or if seated, feel your legs and buttocks firmly connected to the earth, supporting you, holding you in place.

Allow your eyes to flutter closed. Take a slow breath in for two to four seconds and a slow breath out for two to four seconds. As you continue to inhale and exhale, place a hand on your abdomen and feel the breath expand your belly under your hand and then slowly exhale, allowing your stomach to relax.

Feel your body relax further into your feet and bring your awareness to your body from head to toe. As you breathe in, contract your muscles in your arms, chest, back, face, and jaw and hold for five seconds, as tight as you can. Then as you exhale, soften, and relax. Take a couple of breaths in and out. Now tighten your muscles again; your arms, chest, back, face, jaw, legs, hips, buttocks, abdomen, and feet and hold for five seconds and slowly soften upon exhaling. Allow all your muscles to be soft and relaxed. As you breathe in and out, feel the softness of the earth under your feet. Repeat one more time. Clench everything tightly, and then soften from head to toe. Softer. Even softer. Feel your body softening a little bit more with each exhalation.

Feel your feet on the earth. See if you can feel the vibrations from the ground. Continue to breathe and sense the connection with the earth supporting your body. Notice how your body feels at this moment. Direct your mind to the back of your head at the base of your skull and follow your spine down towards your feet, very slowly, one vertebra at a time through your upper back, middle back, lower back to your tailbone. Now imagine a monkey's tail continuing down from the base of your spine or tailbone and reaching towards the earth between your feet. Visualize this new "tail" or "root," sinking into the earth. Down through the sediment layers with their blue-green, reddish-brown, and yellowish-white hues, going deeper into the vast blue waters, filling yourself up and quenching your thirst. Nearing the center core of the earth, feel the heat from the magnetic core, the intense energy, the enormous strength it offers you with the warmth that soothes your soul. Wrap your tail around the solid, iron core. Secure your tail even tighter. Now gather up all that radiant energy and draw it up through your tail as you return slowly, and gently, guiding that energy upwards towards your body. Returning through the vibrations of the powerful, deep-blue rivers, the stability of the rock and sediment, further up through the green grasses and back to your feet. Draw up the energy, your connection to the earth, the magical waters, up through your spine, and visualize your tail grounded in this glorious energy to feed and strengthen your bones, making them strong. Sending much-needed nutrients into your blood, nerves, lighting up all of your cells to work, and be energized at their highest level. Visualize the lightening between your interconnectedness that makes your body whole.

With your body grounded to the earth, you will now ask yourself a few questions to connect to your intuition. Have a journal or notebook ready to jot down notes. Notice how your body is feeling right now. The critical piece is to notice how your body *feels* versus *thinking* with your mind about how it should feel.

Ask yourself questions that begin with what, how, who, and where. Avoid asking questions that start with why, as those produce fear-related answers that come from thought rather than feeling.

It's important to ask a specific and precise question. If you don't have a specific question, then ask a question for the highest good and intention. One of my favorite questions to ask when I'd like guidance on something is: *What would you like me to know about ____?* Or, *What guidance do you have regarding ____?*

Fill in the blank with a specific topic or circumstance. Be as specific as possible. Be clear and concise with your question. If the question is too long, it may be difficult to hear or understand the answer you receive. Feel how your body responds to each question. If you hear a "yes" response, does your body feel light, relaxed, or peaceful, like a sigh of relief? If, however, the body feels heavy, icky, unsure, just not right, or a pit develops in your stomach, then the answer is "no." Sometimes you can hear an answer, and sometimes you feel the answer. Many times when we are frustrated and afraid, we are looking anxiously for answers. This is understandable, yet all the more important to take the time to become grounded using the tools outlined above. Trust the feeling in your body or the answer you may receive. It might come via sound, sight, smell, taste, and/or a gut feeling or knowing. Are you listening to your body? Or are you thinking about what it *should* feel like?

Trust what comes to you and what feels right to you. This is your intuition. With trust in the answers you receive, your intuition, you are empowering yourself. This will lead to an awakening of your intuitive awareness and open psychic doorways. Doubt is fear. Fear is your ego, attempting to rationalize. Trust what you receive and the meaning you perceive. Ask your Guides or Spirit to show you signs or messages to increase your awareness. What do you feel, hear, or see? These may show up as sounds, images. Many signs show up in nature, birds circling overhead or dive-bombing in front of you, a large raven with his impressive stature watching or you hear it's deep throaty "kraa" calls. Notice what is happening or what you think when you see a "sign" or message in nature, like a snapshot in time.

There are many different ways to connect with your intuition. For more ideas, check out my resource page: https://intuitive-bodytherapeutics.com/resources/

Connecting to intuition is transformative. That connection lies in our ability to see the light within what is sometimes perceived as darkness. Energetically it will allow you to connect with your highest self. Trust the flow of guidance.

Finally, notice sequences of numbers, especially consecutive numbers, such as 111, or 333. These are angel numbers and have a specific vibrational meaning or guidance from the divine. If an animal shows its presence to you physically or in a dream state, there is symbolic wisdom. Let the powerful messages deepen your awareness. Nature, spirit animals, and numbers can often be a catalyst for messages to appear. When something catches your attention, listen to see what messages reveal themselves. Stop what you are doing to be fully present and hear the subtle and not-so-subtle signs. Messages with a sense of urgency may compel you to do or say something that is totally out of character for you. Like my deer in the headlights on that wildlife preserve, this is precisely the guidance that can save and transform our lives.

---

**Tina Serocke, MOT, OTR/L, is the owner of Intuitive Body Therapeutics, where her focus is on integrating body, mind, soul, and spirit to help you on your healing journey. Her healing sessions are custom designed to release those places that may have kept clients "stuck" for years. As an intuitive healer, energy medicine practitioner, and occupational therapist, she will help guide you to reach your goals and dreams using Myofascial Release therapy, intuitive guidance and channeling, mediumship, and therapeutic touch therapy. Using this variety of healing modalities, she incorporates a highly customized**

and effective approach to each person. This approach is profoundly empowering for her clients along their transformative healing journey using her psychic gifts.

In her spare time, Tina enjoys learning about healthy food combinations that feed her body, the beach and ocean, traveling, reading, and using her arsenal of grounding meditation and centering exercises to stay focused and healthy in mind, body, and spirit. She works and lives in the Chicago area and offers local and distance healing. Using love and compassion to guide you on your journey for spiritual awakening, you can connect with her at www.IntuitiveBodyTherapeutics.com

CHAPTER 4

# Showing Up

## A Tool for Self-Acceptance and Love

BY LORI CALVO, MHSA, NBC-HWC

I've been on a journey of healing for as long as I can remember. As I peeked into the shadows and dug a little deeper, I found mySelf. Some things I deemed worthy, like my passion for social justice and my love of Chicago Blues. Other things I wanted to keep hidden, like my tendency to self-medicate and my depression.

I don't recall when I received the official diagnosis of depression. It seems like it was always there, lurking in the deepest parts of me. Showing up at the most inconvenient times.

Depression is invisible. Even close friends may not know when you're dealing with it. When I first started dating my husband, I was in a good place emotionally. But depression was never far away, tapping my shoulder to get my attention. *What will Keith think about me? Who would want to be with me like that? He'll probably leave.* I often wished for an illness people could see because I thought it made it more real and, in my mind, more acceptable.

Depression is clever. It can sneak up on you without warning. It kept me from being fully present in my life and in the lives of others. I worked hard to complete my master's degree and imagined my family beaming with pride at my graduation. When the day came, I doubt they were beaming. They had no idea when it was because I didn't make plans to go.

Depression is annoying. Things that are joyful become chores. I missed so many good times. I canceled plans. I skipped out on parties and didn't show up to weddings. I've known Valerie and Eric since moving back to Maryland. We spend Thanksgiving together every year and consider ourselves family. I still feel the pain and regret of missing their wedding 20 years ago.

Depression kept me still. I lost myself.

Then I realized it could be different. Depression came for a visit when Alicia and I had plans to get together. I tried to cancel. I was even brave enough to tell her it was due to my depression. She so lovingly told me, "It's okay with me. I just want to see you." *What? You want to spend time with me? Like this?*

That conversation was a lifeline. (Alicia, if you're reading this, thank you from the bottom of my heart. You have no idea how much you helped me.)

I was okay as-is. I didn't have to lie, and I didn't have to hide. I tentatively embraced my depression and looked for ways it could serve me.

I changed the terminology. Instead of thinking of it as "being depressed," I reframed it as "having depression." A television commercial referred to people who had diabetes and lived a full life. *You mean I could "have" something without the label of "being" that thing?* While it seems like a subtle shift, it was a game-changer. I no longer felt like a victim. I stopped dismissing myself as just being a little depressed about something. I felt empowered to find ways to manage and thrive.

Yet my journal was full of questions. *Why me? Why do I have to deal with this? What did I do to deserve this?* I started meditating and began to feel more peaceful. Instead of asking "why," I tried on the notion of "things happen for a reason."

If there's a reason, then it must be perfect. The logical next step is we're all perfect, just the way we are, at any given moment. We may be better or worse tomorrow, but we will still be perfect. I may not like something about my interaction with someone. I may even feel hurt or angry. Yet I still believe that person is exactly where they need to be. Perfect for that moment in time.

There was one area where I came up short. While I truly believed in the perfection of others, I most definitely did not believe in my own. I judged myself horribly. I never felt good enough or smart enough. I was too fat, too sarcastic, or too critical. I was, in a word, unlovable.

Perhaps this feels familiar to you. My story includes depression; yours may not. Do you recognize a part of yourself in my words? I understand. I see you. And I believe you're perfect, just as you are.

You may be wondering how I turned it around, how I stopped self-judgment, and replaced it with self-compassion.

I'd love to tell you it's the easiest thing in the world. Not quite. But it is something you can do right now, today. Starting the process takes very little effort.

You've undoubtedly heard the Nike slogan, "Just Do It." It's kind of like that. My slogan (my personal mantra) is, "Just Show Up."

## Just Show Up

These three little words sound simple: Just Show Up. *Okay. Sure. I'll just show up. No problem. Here I am. And?*

I see it as a mindset tool with three main aspects woven together. Each piece works independently, but, taken together, they're a powerful way to take care of you. The tool is a mesh of:

- Accept where you are
- Pause before acting
- Take baby steps

### ACCEPT WHERE YOU ARE

The first part to **Just Show Up** is about acknowledging yourself, however you're feeling. It's a commitment to self-love and accepting yourself exactly as you are in the moment. Depression? That's fine. Unmotivated? That's fine too.

I've also included a bit of surrender here. I let go of my need to control it. I remember I'm okay as-is.

There are many ways to cultivate self-love and acceptance. The ones that have worked best for me are journaling, meditation, and positive affirmations.

### *Journaling*

Putting your thoughts down on paper can be a daunting proposition. I have found it to be a lifesaver. Sometimes I can write for hours. Other times I'm lucky to complete a sentence or two. (Remember to review chapter two for a little more on journaling.)

I encourage you to journal regularly. Daily is ideal. If you're stuck about what to write, try one or all of these to see what works for you:

- At the end of each day, write three things you're grateful for.
- When you wake up in the morning, jot down three things that describe how you want to feel that day.
- Create a poem. Don't worry – it doesn't have to rhyme.
- Spend time writing about a challenge you've had. Be as detailed as possible. What happened? What were you thinking? How were you feeling?
- Decide how long you're going to write and set a timer. Three minutes? Five minutes? Write whatever flows out of you until the timer goes off.
- When words won't come, doodle instead.

### *Meditation*

Ah, meditation. It makes you feel completely comfortable and at ease, or it fills you with dread thinking about sitting in silence with just your thoughts. Admittedly, I initially fell into the second category. I could barely sit still for one minute before my thoughts came racing through. *What should I make for dinner? Don't forget the oil change. Please make that dog downstairs stop barking!*

And then I realized there are many kinds of meditation, and I didn't have to sit in silence. Here are a few options you might try:

- Guided meditation. Sit comfortably and focus on someone else speaking rather than the running commentary in your head. Examples include:
    - Body scan meditation for grounding or sleep.
    - Loving-kindness meditation for compassion.
    - Relaxation meditation for pain management.
- Walking meditation. Instead of sitting still, you can meditate while walking. Examples include:
    - Focus on your breath. Inhale for four steps. Hold the breath for four. Exhale for four. Hold for four. Repeat.
    - Focus on your surroundings. What colors are the leaves on the trees? What does the breeze feel like? What songs are the birds singing?
    - Focus on your steps. Slowly place your heal down. Roll your foot forward from the heel to the toes. Lift off from the toes. Repeat.
- Mantra meditation. To keep your thoughts from wandering, choose a sound to repeat silently with each inhalation. The word may or may not have any meaning. Examples include:
    - Love.
    - Om.
    - I am.

### *Positive Affirmations*

A short statement written in the present tense that describes how you want to be is the general definition of a positive affirmation. Writing them down and speaking them out loud has helped me change my negative head-talk and given me clarity and focus. You can create what works best for your specific situation. Here are a few to get you started:

- My opinion matters.
- I wake up every morning feeling well-rested and refreshed.
- I am lovable.

## PAUSE BEFORE ACTING

The second facet to **Just Show Up** breaks the chain of going on auto-pilot and possibly choosing poorly. When I take the time to pause, I immediately stop myself from going down a path that doesn't support me.

Stop right where you are. Take a breath. Ask yourself what will serve you best.

But what if one quick breath isn't enough? We breathe all day every day without giving it any thought. The beautiful thing about that is if we become more mindful about breathing, it can bring comfort and peace.

I regularly tell my students breathing is the best mindfulness practice because it can be done anywhere and at any time. Even one minute is valuable.

There are many options to a breathing practice. The simplest one is to focus on the existing pattern of your breathing. Notice how you breathe in. Is it a deep breath? Or more shallow? Notice how you breathe out. Is it slow and measured? Or fast and abrupt? There's no right or wrong. Just notice.

## TAKE BABY STEPS

The third part to **Just Show Up** is the action. Think about what you can do at this moment to shift to a more uplifted position. In moments of depression, I sometimes want to stay closed, curled up, and away from others. There are times when tending to myself that way is the best course of action, and I honor that decision.

More often than not, however, I have to find a way to connect with myself and with other people. As I'm writing this, I recall how hard this was to do when I first tried it. It took all my attention and energy to make even tiny steps in the right direction.

Everything changed the day I decided to rely on my practices to love and accept myself just where I was. I paused and stopped the autopilot from kicking in and sending an email about having to miss an online gathering of colleagues and friends. Being free of the autopilot gave me the courage to sign into the meeting. While I knew most of the people on the call, I still felt exposed. So, I put on a pair of funky purple reading glasses, took a deep breath, and turned on the camera on my computer.

When it was my turn to say hello, I shared that I wasn't feeling great, and the best I could do that day was show up. I made no promises beyond that. To my amazement, my colleagues and friends welcomed me just as I was. *Wow!* They were happy I joined them.

Later that same month, I had another scheduled meeting. This one in person. *Ugh. I can't do this. Who would want me there?* I remembered the online meeting and followed the same process. Once again, to my surprise, my colleagues and friends appreciated me being there.

I continued practicing showing up. I did it for work. I did it for social events. I did it for my family. Most importantly, I did it for mySelf.

The concept of being perfect right where we are plays a big role in all my relationships and has become a pillar of my work as a wholeness coach. I invite you to try it—even just a little bit. I'd love to hear how you **Just Show Up**.

---

Lori's Bachelor of Arts in Psychology and Master's in Health Services Administration led to an excellent career in Process Improvement and Provider Relations Management. After a series of layoffs, she realized the career she loved and had worked so hard to build was no longer a reality.

Lori successfully turned this into a positive and enrolled in the Health and Wellness Coaching program at the Maryland University of Integrative Health (MUIH). Shortly after graduating from MUIH in 2015, Lori joined the International Coaching Federation (ICF), serving on the Membership and Communications Committees. She also joined the MUIH faculty in the Health and Wellness Coaching program—first as a teaching assistant and then as a mentor coach. In 2017 she was among the first group of coaches to become nationally board certified by the National Board for Health & Wellness Coaching (NBHWC). And in 2019, she earned the rank of adjunct faculty at MUIH as an instructor for the Foundations of Healthy Lifestyles course.

Using her expertise in wholeness coaching and skills as a Reiki practitioner, Lori is honored to serve brave men and women who are ready to show up in their lives and thrive.

A reformed soda drinker who always had a pink TaB can in her hand, Lori now sticks to cold brew coffee and Earl Grey tea. You can connect with Lori at www.justshowupcoaching.com

CHAPTER 5

# Awakening Intuition

## The Key to Success with Reiki

BY DR. ALICE LANGHOLT, PH.D.

I'm a Reiki Master Teacher with a Ph.D. in Metaphysical Parapsychology, who runs an online school for intuitive development. But, I didn't know anything about intuition or energy healing until I was 38 years old. I was, at the time, a fairly "regular" person, though I would also describe myself as "spiritually frustrated" back then. I was working as a Jewish Educator, full time, for a large temple in Cleveland, Ohio. I had been offered that job and the chance to earn a Master's Degree in Jewish Studies at a full scholarship through a program funded by the Jewish community and thought it sounded like a good deal, so I had taken it. I completed my degree and was doing a lot of teaching, ran a Jewish youth theater with original full-scale musicals, and was immersed in the job for nine years.

During that time, part of me felt like an imposter. Sure, I could do all of the things required of me. I could read and teach Hebrew, knew all about the holidays, I could play my guitar, and enthusiastically lead a song session. I could sit with a group of seventh graders at a service and keep them focused on participating in the prayers. But, I was secretly wondering if there was a point to it all. I didn't feel sure that any of it mattered. I had no true spiritual connection because I didn't have any *experience* to go along with all of these actions.

The Rabbi of my temple was a very friendly, approachable, and charismatic guy who had spiritual confidence that I not only admired, but I felt nagging jealousy about. He was just so comfortable in his role. I wanted that but didn't know how to get it. What I wanted was to actually feel something that I could know was outside of my mundane thoughts and day to day life. I wanted to feel something spiritual, not once, but consistently and reliably. I wanted *connection.* Thinking of myself then, I would describe myself as *spiritually thirsty.*

I didn't know anything about intuition or energy healing back then. If asked, I would have said it was something that people gifted with psychic abilities had, but I didn't. I had never heard of Reiki.

Then, one day, obviously pregnant with my fourth child, I was picking up my older two children from school, and a parent approached me. "You're pregnant," she said. Impressed with her knack for the obvious, I nodded that she was correct. "Well, you should learn Reiki," she stated.

"What's that? Rake the leaves?" I asked, confused, thinking she had said, "raking."

"No," she laughed, "It's an energy healing method that can reduce pregnancy discomforts and help you in labor." Now she had my attention. I mean, those are attention-grabbing words to someone who is pregnant, let alone with their fourth kid.

"You've got my attention," I said, "What is it?" She went on to tell me that she could teach me, and I could come to her house and learn this technique. The spiritually thirsty part of me was very interested, especially, and before long, I was at her house to learn Reiki.

I'd like to say that this was a pivotal moment for me, but it wasn't. Despite her gift at pitching Reiki to potential students, she just wasn't the kind of teacher I needed. She did teach me hand positions. She gave me an attunement (a ritual transfer of the energetic ability to do Reiki). But, she didn't give me what I really needed: understanding *how* to experience the energy. She just gave me lots of things to *do.* She gave me didactical knowledge of hand positions and instructions to hold my hands at each place for three to five minutes. She didn't tell me what would happen, what to expect, or how to recognize and observe the energy. When I asked, she told me to just do the things and not to be concerned with feeling anything.

I was ambivalent about my ability to use Reiki. I tried self-healing but wasn't sure I was doing it right, or if it was working. Basically, I thought I wasn't good enough, or psychic enough, or whatever special quality was required to do Reiki. I just didn't have it.

Fast forward a year and a half. I was back at school, baby in tow, and I saw my teacher. I asked her, "By the way, is there any more to this Reiki stuff, because I'm not very good at it?"

"Oh yes," she replied casually, "You should learn level two. It's much stronger."

At that moment, I didn't know if I wanted to hug her, or hit her. On the one hand, that little spark of hope inside me that I really could have an experience of something more was still there. On the other hand, she waited a year and a half to tell me this?! I took a deep breath and expressed interest, and before long, I was back at her house to learn level two.

Now there were symbols to learn. And, they were complicated, Japanese Kanji with up to 25 strokes and five-syllable names. I had to practice and take a symbol test. Also, there was another attunement, which again, I didn't feel or understand. I was pretty discouraged. After passing my symbol test, I was getting up to leave.

While putting on my sweater, I made a comment. It meant nothing to me at the time; it was one of those throwaway kinds of comments that didn't need to be said aloud, like, "My nose is itching." But what I said was, "My hands are tingling." I thought nothing of it. I thought that I had held my wrist funny or something, and this was a blood flow sensation. I didn't even know why I had said it.

"Yes, that's the energy," my teacher said.

"What? No," I said dismissively.

"Your hands are tingling," she said.

I had figured she had heard me wrong, but she hadn't. "Yes, I probably held my wrist funny or something."

"That's the energy," she repeated.

"No, it isn't."

She told me to follow her, and she lay down on her massage table. "Scan me," she commanded. I knew what that meant, but had never done it before. She meant for me to move my hands above her body, from head to toe, not touching, and tell her what I felt.

I was sorry I had said anything and expected nothing to happen. At first, nothing did, except the thoughts in my head about how dumb I felt were giving me plenty to listen to. And then, when my hands were over her hip, I felt a tingle. I moved them forward, and the tingling stopped. I moved them over her hip, and it started again. I pulled them back, and the tingling stopped.

I had to ask. "All right... Why are my hands tingling here, and not here or here?"

"Because your hands are over my hip, and it hurts. I twisted it or something this morning," she answered, matter-of-factly.

"You're telling me that my hands are tingling because you have pain?" I asked incredulously.

"Yes," she answered as if it was no big deal. But it was a big deal. It was huge for me. I was feeling a physical sensation related to her pain *without touching her.* I now refer to this as my "tingle moment." It was the moment when I realized there was something to observe, and I wanted to know more. Not only that, but I had a palpable feeling of relief – there *is* something that connects me to outside of my body – spiritual energy – and I can interact with it.

I needed to know if it would ever happen again, if it would be consistent, if it would work with other people, and what else I could learn. From that moment, I started experimenting and observing my tingles. As I learned more about Reiki (and took level 3 at a nearby college), my tingles started to become different. Sometimes sharp, sometimes feathery, sometimes static-like, the tingles would change. I started to realize these sensations were relative to what the recipient of the Reiki was feeling or going through. For example, I'd feel prickly tingles if the person had pain. I'd feel static-like tingles if the person was grieving over something.

My tingles were a language spoken by my intuition, and I was learning to understand it! I was learning this language by repetition, observation, and connecting the dots once I'd had enough experience. This is the organic way that language is learned by a baby. The more I would tune in and observe my tingles, the more I'd notice.

I learned that this is called Clairsentience, and it is one of the intuitive senses. Most of all, learning to observe what comes to me and to make these connections opened the door to strengthening my intuition. The other intuitive senses, (Clairvoyance, Clairaudience, and Claircognizance) do the same for those of us who have learned to simply observe their messages.

This experience was what drove me to continue to learn and grow my Reiki practice and then branch out into learning and using other intuitive tools. Most of all, my excitement at learning that my intuition was, in fact, talking to me, led me to want to show others that they can learn the same thing. When I teach Reiki, the first part I teach my students is how to recognize their intuition's signals.

I wrote up an Observation Exercise that is useful for anyone who wants to start to tune in to what is already there.

Here's what to do:

Spend five minutes just sitting still and observing yourself and everything around you. Tune in to your own body, your emotions, the external sensory input (sights, sounds, physical sensations, scents, tastes) that are part of your experience. Notice what emotions you are feeling right now. Do not try to shut anything out, rather just observe all that you experience and feel. When five minutes are up, write down what you observed.

Doing this exercise allows your left brain (the chatty part) to focus on taking mental notes of the sensory stimuli, which comes from the right brain (where your intuition lives). The left brain is the analytical part, and the right brain is creative, empathetic, and intuitive. This exercise starts to get them working together in a way that supports intuitive development.

Practicing this exercise helps you be ready to learn Reiki, and right away, recognize the way the energy is communicating through your intuition. You will easily feel your attunement working, and you will easily work with the healing energy. (You won't need a year and a half of ambivalence, as I had!)

I encourage you to learn Reiki energy healing, and also to allow your interests to take you farther. My life has opened up dramatically, my intuition has taken a confident hold, and I now have a spiritual connection that I had longingly searched for. You can experience life-altering results too!

There's also an easier way to learn Reiki now, called Practical Reiki. It doesn't use symbols or hand positions. It's simple, sensible, and powerful. You can learn it online at www.PracticalReiki.org or find more to open to at www.ReikiAwakeningAcademy.com.

---

**Dr. Alice Langholt, Ph.D., is a parent, author, and teacher with Master level training in several Reiki modalities, and a Certified EFT Practitioner. She teaches classes in Reiki and intuitive development locally and by distance. She is the Executive Director of Reiki Awakening Academy Online School of Intuitive Development.**

**Alice has a Ph.D. in Metaphysical Parapsychology, and Master's degrees in Jewish Studies and Metaphysical Science. Alice is the author of the award-winning Reiki resource, *Practical Reiki: for balance, well-being, and vibrant health. A guide to a simple, revolutionary energy healing method,* which won second place for Best Reiki Book in the 2012 About.com Reader's Choice Awards, and was a finalist in the 2017 Books of Excellence Awards, as well as 11 other books on holistic subjects. Living in the Washington, DC Metro area with her husband and four children, Alice teaches Animal Reiki at Montgomery College, has a Reiki practice, and is also a wedding officiant. Find out more at AliceLangholt.com.**

CHAPTER 6

# Simple Meditation

## Quiet the Mind and Heal the Body

BY DR. SHELLEY ASTROF, M.ED., D.MEDITATION

## My Story

"The cause of world is mind." It was 1978, and cassette recorders were all the rage. My husband and I were pregnant and attending a group meditation. I remember closing my eyes and hearing the words, "The cause of world is mind." That was the first time I listened to the voice of my Teacher. He definitely caught my attention.

That opening line was the start of a most extraordinary talk. My Teacher's words spoke deep into my soul. My mind didn't have a clear understanding, but every fiber of my being knew he was speaking the truth. At that moment, I knew I found the purpose of my life. It would take many more years for my mind and life to catch up to what I knew at that moment.

Meditation is an ancient practice. In Sanskrit, it's called Dhyan Yoga. It refers to the entire process of evolving the intelligence of a human being to the state of Self-realization, the Knower state of consciousness.

In the 1970s, my husband and I were young and had promising careers. He was in MBA school, and I was an elementary school teacher. Education was one of my loves. But that's another story.

This story is about my love for meditation.

My husband began meditating after reading a sign in the university, saying, "Improve your marks. Learn to meditate." He attended the meeting and became a regular meditator. And he did well in school.

Later on, he joined a meditation group. I was a more casual meditator at the time. He urged me to come with him to the meditation center. He said, "You should come. They really know something." My husband was a clear thinker, and I was a skeptic. But at that moment we both heard the truth knocking at our door and we just opened it. It still amazes me how my life turned out. I will always be grateful to him for introducing me to meditation, my Teacher, and a life fulfilled. I agreed to attend the group meditation.

The first time I went to the center, I was a few months pregnant. It was a most extraordinary experience and one that changed the course of my life. When I entered the room, everyone appeared familiar. It was more like a meeting of long-forgotten friends rather than people I had never met before.

I remember walking over to look at a large photo of their Teacher. I stood staring at the image; I have no idea for how long. As I stood mesmerized, engulfed in the most profound sense of calm and quiet, I felt like I was being welcomed into my long-forgotten real home.

From that moment onwards, I started meditating regularly with the group. I would listen to recordings of our Teacher's talks and read his books. It was as if I had been starving for so long that I didn't even know that I was hungry. His words were my food, and they were nourishing my soul. That was where I first heard the words, "The cause of world is mind."

When my son was two years old, I enrolled in graduate school. After my first year, my husband and I were having financial troubles, and I thought I should look for a paying job. I went to the university to let them know that I would be withdrawing from the program. I wrote to my Teacher to let him know.

I quit on a Friday, and Saturday morning, I received a telegram. There was no internet in those days. The telegram read, "A perfectionist finishes the task only for knowing that he's perfect and no gain. Thus, continue studies and finish."

I went back to the Dean's office on Monday morning to see if I could undo what I had done. When the secretary saw me, she said, "I never told the Dean that you were quitting. I only told her that you were having financial difficulties. She's in her office waiting for you."

If I hadn't believed in divine intervention before, it was now staring me in the face.

I can remember walking out of the Dean's office with an RA job (Research Assistant), a TA job (Teaching Assistant), and a full professorship to teach B.Ed. off-campus courses. And I was given an office.

My financial situation was taken care of. Now I had to learn how to juggle time. I had my classes with their course loads, three jobs, a child, a husband, and a household. Time was something that was in short supply.

It was at this time that I learned about different styles of meditation and how each method would produce different results.

**Mantra meditation:** In graduate school, I really needed my intellect to be sharp and alert. Time was of the essence, and during those years, I practiced mantra meditation primarily. I used to work for about 2 hours and then meditate on mantra for 15-30 minutes. When I would open my eyes, I was refreshed and able to put in another two full-on hours. When deadlines were due, I would follow this pattern of 2 hours of work and 15-30 minutes of meditation through the night. I used the mantra *Amaram Hum Madhuram Hum*. It translates as "I am immortal, I am blissful."

**Pranayama meditation:** When I would feel emotional, or my mind would make me uneasy, then I would watch my breath in meditation. Pranayama helped center my mind because the movement of breath is linked to the movement of the mind. That is why calming the breath helps calm the mind.

**Knower meditation:** In Knower meditation, I would close my eyes and watch the thoughts come and go without becoming involved in their content. I observed that my thoughts were always changing. Then I'd place my attention on the watcher of the changing thoughts. The one watching is the authentic Self, the Knower. When I put my attention on the Knower in meditation, I could feel a power getting built at the core of my being.

Meditation is essential to quiet the mind and heal the body. It helps build great power in you. When you add to your meditation, the knowledge of the mind (as changing), and the Knower (as unchanging), you usher in fresh and powerful courage.

More than 40 years have come and gone since I began my journey in meditation. These words, "The cause of world is mind," have served me well throughout my life. They've been with me and helped me when I had to deal with all kinds of nonsense.

Quite some years ago, I felt abandoned and betrayed by my husband and my parents. I tried everything I knew to keep myself afloat. I would close my eyes and watch my breath, repeat mantra, watch my mind. I did anything not to feel the invasion of their negative judgment. I could feel their opinions, starting to impact my mental and physical health.

My saving grace was continuing to ponder and meditate on the phrase, "The cause of world is mind." I began to seriously look inside. I wondered about the cause of the downfall of my world. *Was it really my mind?*

My Teacher encouraged us to meditate and study our own mind; to observe the patterns of our thinking process. So, I did.

Over time I came to understand that everyone's mind, including my own, has its own unique way of thinking and concluding. And everyone's thinking mind keeps changing. I kept thinking; *there was a time when my husband and parents thought I was terrific. I'm still the same person, but now they don't like me.*

Through watching my mind in meditation, I realized there was nothing I could do about other people's thoughts and ideas. But I could do something about my own.

I watched as my mind began siding with other people's negative opinions about me. My own mind was actually bullying me. I had to find a way to make my mind, my friend, and stop this harassment. It was enough to deal with bullying from my outside world. This realization is what sparked my turn-around, this is how I began to heal.

I realized that I had to build my strength and confidence from the inside. From studying my mind, I knew its triggers. So, watching my mind in meditation gave me the power to understand how to weather the storms. I couldn't make the storm stop, but I could buy an umbrella.

As a result, I found the strength and courage to stand for myself; those who cared about me started to see ME. I had grown in confidence, was less reactive, and utterly unapologetic about the choices I made for my life. In time my husband became my well-wisher and friend. My mom came to really appreciate me. And before my dad passed away, his last words to me were, "I want you to know that I am very proud of you, and I'm proud of what you're doing!"

Our life is a work in progress. We can bring greater joy and delight to ourselves and our loved ones if we practice the knowledge of meditation. In our meditation, we can include the knowledge of the mind as changing, and the knowledge of the authentic Knower as unchanging. Then meditation will become a method of educating the mind. It will give you tremendous power of understanding that will serve you and your loved ones for your whole life.

## The Tool

I have prepared two Knower Meditations that are unique and straightforward. You can read each meditation into a recording device and then listen back as you close your eyes, or you can have someone read it to you. You can listen to these Knower Meditations for FREE on my website Resource page. https://www.knower.ca/resources.

## Knower Meditation on Thoughts

Make a comfortable seat anywhere and close your eyes.

You might find that at the back of your closed eyes, thoughts appear.

Just watch your thoughts appear in your mind, and know that watching them, doesn't make them appear.

Thoughts come by themselves; they come uninvited.

Thoughts appear, they will stay for some time, and then they'll go. You don't have to interfere with their comings and goings.

You are the one who is knowing that the thoughts are there. So, you are the Knower of the thoughts in your mind.

Let the thoughts come and let the thoughts go. Just remain watching.

Thoughts appear, they'll change into thoughts that disappear. So thoughts are changing.

But you, the Knower who watches them, is unchanging.

Let's focus on the unchanging Knower.

Just watch as the thoughts do their thing.

Stay with the one who is watching, stay with your own Self, the unchanging Knower.

Take some time to be with your own well-being, the Knower.

## Knower Meditation on Memory

Make a comfortable seat anywhere and close your eyes.

Your eyes will know that there is nothing in front of them. Yet, in your mind, the memory of things and people is still there.

All that is known by the mind and senses is filtered into the mind; it's processed, understood, and made into a formed, mental, believable reality.

Memory is a human mental sense.

The mind sees through memory even when the eyes are closed and not seeing outwardly.

While you are sitting in meditation, the mind may carry on thinking for some time.

The purpose of Knower meditation is to wait and watch and observe the mind's patterns. As if they were clouds in the sky of the mind or characters on a television screen who are just figures of light.

The one who is watching and knowing the mind is your own Self, the Knower.

So sit quietly, watch, and wait. Whatever thoughts, memories, or ideas that have come will also go. Be with the one who is watching, knowing, and never changing. That is the Knower. Be with the Knower.

You can meditate for some time.

## Meditation for Children

Meditation is a place where children can find peace, happiness, and sunshine within. Where the clouds of the mind can't reach because they are in the sky and above the mind's clouds.

It's important for children to feel safe and happy with the idea of meditation. It would be wonderful if children fell in love with closing their eyes; they'd come back to meditation on their own if their experience was pleasant and welcoming. Meditation is a space or sanctuary where they can know that they are totally protected and safe from outside hindrances.

When children are young, you can let them sit in your lap or sit beside you to meditate for however long they are able. In this way, they'll feel safe, protected, and loved as they learn that there's a delight in sitting still.

I have three Smile Meditations available for FREE on my website. They give children the association of meditation with smiling and being happy. https://www.knower.ca/

I wrote a holistic approach to education and meditation; it was a book my Teacher encouraged me to write. *The Knower Curriculum* contains nine insightful stories, meditation ideas, breathing exercises, mantra sounds and meanings, hatha yoga poses, along with games and activities. It's a complete program to develop the mind, spirit, and body awareness of children and grown-ups alike.

There is also a companion book called *Timeless Tales*, a story-book/coloring book of the stories from *The Knower Curriculum*.

Using the design of the curriculum, I developed an online club, *The Knower Club*. It's a place where you and your child can spend hours engaged in activities from *The Knower Curriculum*. The powerful tools will build in your child a sense of self-confidence and empowerment. You can check it out on my website. https://www.knower.ca/

---

**Shelley Astrof is a Doctor of Meditation and Peace Pioneer with extensive experience and training in education (M.Ed.). She holds a Certificate of Advanced Studies in Yog Science, Vedant Philosophy, and the Theory and Practice of Meditation. She can help you get grounded in Self-awareness and connect with your inner guidance and sense of well-being, the Knower. With four decades in association with a Meditation Master in the Himalayas of India, she offers a unique perspective on the value of meditation and growth of awareness. Her mission is to give you that solid foundation and trust in your being, the Knower of who you are.**

**She's a mom, taught elementary school, and University level B.Ed. classes. She's the author of *The Knower Curriculum* and *Timeless Tales.* These are books her Meditation teacher encouraged her to develop as a fresh approach to education and meditation. They are excellent resources for you.**

**If she's not roaming the picturesque hills and pathways of the Himalayas, you might find her sipping tea and singing Sanskrit verses from the Bhagavad Gita with her friends. She has a website where you can find out about her adventures in meditation and awareness. You're always welcome to drop by. https://www.knower.ca/.**

## CHAPTER 7

# Grounding and Centering

## Clarity Through Heart Connection

BY CAROLYN MCGEE, CLC, MNST, CRM, EFT

I was ten years old, playing with my cousins in the river behind my grandparents' home when I got swept away and almost drowned. That was the moment I lost my connection with my intuition.

Do you remember a moment where this was taken away from you? Or you started to doubt yourself?

An uncle pulled me from the freezing water after about 30 minutes. During that long 30 minutes, I started to doubt myself. I lost my confidence in my choices. I forgot I could connect to angels and animals. My fear overrode my feelings. I lost myself.

I spent years looking outside of myself for validation and searching for who I was. I lost my connection to who I truly was at my core. I couldn't see or feel my heart and soul. I allowed fear to drive my choices. I tried to fit into other's expectations and lost myself even more.

I returned to a childhood pattern of focusing on helping people and making a difference to be seen. As a small child, I loved being the teacher's helper and made sure everyone was included. I taught my stuffed animals to read. I wanted to be a doctor and heal people. Unfortunately, my aversion to blood made being a doctor impractical. My next choice was social worker. My parents talked me out of that as I wouldn't make any money. So, I followed my fear of being different and went to college for engineering. I followed the logical path instead of my heart and soul's guidance.

As I started my corporate career, my office was always the stopping place for advice and support. I was a great listener and continued my passion for helping others. I hadn't yet learned the power of setting good boundaries and caring for my energy as much as I cared for others. Putting others' needs first became a bad habit that took a toll on my health.

After a painful divorce, I channeled my fear of not being able to help others into healing myself. I knew I needed to break the pattern of following convention and other's guidance instead of my heart. Seeing my children look up to me gave me the courage to see myself as I truly am instead of the version I presented to the world.

I started to meditate, work with the healing vibration of color, and became a Reiki Master Teacher. Learning to connect to and understand my energy and the vibration of energy around me started my journey back to loving me.

When I started my pet care business after being let go from my corporate job, I felt empowered. While I cared for my clients and their pets, I also made myself a priority. I slowly started to heal and allow the real me to be seen.

My connection with animals deepened, and I felt my energy become more tangible, grounded, and present. It was during this time that I rediscovered my connection to the Angels and the Divine.

During meditation, I remembered that Archangel Ariel was with me in that river many years ago. She shielded me with her wings from the freezing water and enveloped me with love and protection. I felt peace and safety at a level I had never experienced. I realized I was being called to share the love and connection of Angels with others and that this was the next step in my healing journey.

As I created my Intuition Coaching business, my old friend fear visited again. I had given away advice and support since I was a child. *"Who did I think I was to now charge for it?"* I remembered how much I love to help others and knew deep in my soul that if I didn't do this, then someone would suffer as I did. This channeled my fear into action.

I genuinely believe that we each have a unique purpose and flavor to our work. This belief motivated me when fear said, *"No one will listen."* I replied, *"No one else can deliver my message as I can. I know there are thousands of people searching for what I uniquely offer. They will have taken many self-help classes, hired coaches, and attended workshops, but still, feel something missing. I must speak and allow them to find me."*

I opened my second business as an Intuitive Coach and Teacher to help others shortcut their journey to connection and inspired action. Learning how to manage my time and energy with my personal life and two growing businesses was another energetic shift towards healing my heart.

Each time I stretched myself personally or professionally, I felt my energy and vibration rise. It was another journey and expansion for me to understand the different energies I had to work with and work within to manage and create these businesses.

The energy required for the pet care business is much more grounded and tactical. It's more in the divine masculine paradigm. It's loving and caring, but it's also producing and acting. The intuitive coaching business is more within the divine feminine energy. It's more creative and focuses on receiving the downloads of how to serve my clients best.

I realized I had much more experience with the divine masculine energy with my engineering and high tech background. I again had the opportunity to step into my fear of being different, to embrace the divine feminine model of faith, receiving and being of service while also serving myself. The days of caring for others at my expense were over.

I enjoyed the cosmic dance of knowing which energy to step into at each moment. Learning how to deepen my receiving ability and when to step into producing energy has allowed me to expand exponentially. I understand how to tap into those different energies on a much more conscious basis.

I used my heart as the center and gauge for my decisions, balance, and growth. I practiced grounding my energy and allowing my heart to make the optimum choices for my soul's growth.

I now embrace my uniqueness and passion for serving as a gift to myself and the world!

One of the beautiful gifts I received from my angels on my journey was a meditation to connect heaven and earth, ground my energy, and center my choices through my heart. My gift to you is to share this exercise.

## The Tool

**Getting Started:** This exercise is most powerful when sitting with your spine as straight as possible and your feet on the ground.

Start by taking three deep breaths in through your nose and out your mouth. Gently close your eyes and bring to your mind a single flame. A bright, white flicker of light.

Breathe that vision into your third eye. Feel the energy pulsing and allow it to become three dimensional and start to move. See it pulse in the action of grace, movement, and fluidity.

**Connect to Mother Earth:** Allow your flame to drop down the chakra line (your spinal column), feeling it moving past your throat, heart, solar plexus, sacral chakra, and down into your root.

With your next breath, allow that flame to drop out of your body and journey down through the earth. See it moving towards the center of the earth, to that molten lava center, the heartbeat of Mother Earth. Watch it connect to that divine feminine energy pulsing at the center of the earth and allow that flame to plug into that molten lava center.

See the flame become fully infused with that red, orange, and yellow energy of Mother Earth. The flame stays distinct, but it becomes infused and gathers that brilliant red, orange, and yellow energy.

Breathe in that divine feminine energy. Slowly bring that fully infused flame back from the center of the earth, through all the layers of the earth and back into your body.

**Root Chakra:** Feel it nestled in your root chakra, vibrant with that red, orange, and yellow energy of the divine feminine. See that entire area of your root chakra from your hips out to the edge of your energetic field, down to below your feet.

See it start to glow red, clearing and releasing thoughts and beliefs of, *I don't belong, I don't fit in. People leave me. I must do this alone. I don't know who my tribe is.* Letting all that energy just fade away, absorbed into that red light.

Breathe in comfort, protection, and safety. The complete foundational understanding of who you are, where you fit in the world, and who your real soul tribe is. Integrate that radiant energy into your body.

**Sacral Chakra:** With your next breath, bring that flame fully infused with the divine feminine energy up to your sacral chakra. As it goes into this area, feel the entire area start to glow orange both inside your body and out to the edge of your energetic field.

As you breathe in this orange light, you are releasing distractions, disconnection, addictions, fear, and loss. Gently allow all those energies to be absorbed entirely into this beautiful orange energy.

Start to breathe in creativity, passion, abundance, a clear understanding of who you are here to serve, and amplifying joy. All these powerful energies are embedding into your Sacral Chakra in that beautiful glowing energy of orange.

**Solar Plexus Chakra:** With your next breath, move that fully infused flame with the red, orange, and yellow energy up to your solar plexus. See the entire solar plexus area start to glow yellow inside and outside your physical body. Your whole solar plexus is filled with vibrant yellow energy.

Release and remove lack of boundaries, confusion, shame, fear that you are not good enough, and the need to make things happen.

Allow that yellow energy to amplify that "No" is a complete sentence, that setting a boundary is a gift to not only you but also the other people who have lessons to learn. Know you have a clear understanding of what is optimal for you and your life purpose and that you always make the right choices.

**Heart Step 1:** With your next breath, bring that fully infused flame with the red, orange, and yellow energy up into your heart. Take a deep breath and release the divine feminine energy into your heart, leaving that red, orange, and yellow energy in your heart.

**Father Sky:** Allow the flame to continue its journey, past your throat, past your third eye into your crown, and then out of your body to exactly 36 inches above your head. See that flame resting in the belly of a star, a star that burns as bright as ten thousand suns.

Feel that flame sit in the star of the divine masculine, Father Sky vibration, becoming powerfully infused with that brilliant white energy. Breathe that in for a moment.

**Crown Chakra:** Bring that brilliant Father Sky energy back into your crown. See your crown open, and the entire area glow purple, both inside and outside your body.

Allow that fully infused flame to burn away any rigid viewpoints, any ego fears, and the concept of I am alone and not supported.

Releasing those ideas that do not serve you and creating a clear channel to divine inspiration. Know that there is always divine support available; all you need to do is ask. Open your connection even more to divine love, light, and inspiration,

**Third Eye Chakra:** With your next breath, bring that fully infused light with the divine masculine flame into your third eye. Seeing your third eye glow indigo throughout your entire third eye area.

See your third eye open wide to allow clearing away any blockages to inspiration, any fears of what you see, what you don't see, and what those messages mean.

Magnify intuition, imagination, visualization, clear and vivid dreams, and understanding of patterns in your life and exactly what they mean.

**Throat Chakra:** With your next breath, bring that flame fully infused with the divine masculine energy down into your throat and see it glow a cobalt blue both inside and outside your body.

It is clearing away any fear of not being heard, misunderstandings, lies, not being clear to yourself or others, and confusion of your message and how to articulate it to others.

Breathe in authenticity, heart-centered communication, keen listening skills, clarity, and understanding, knowing that you can always speak your truth and that will be received from a loving place.

**Heart Chakra:** Bring that fully infused with the divine masculine flame back into your heart and see your entire heart chakra glow green to the edge of your aura. See the divine masculine and divine feminine coming together in joy, creating an explosion of love, clarity, and peace in your heart.

These energies burn away fear, guilt, grief, and shame. Releasing not good enough, not trying enough, rejection, and I must do it myself into this beautiful connection of the divine masculine and the divine feminine. Your heart fills with that beautiful green, vibrant light infused with the brilliant white light and joy of Father Sky and Mother Earth.

See that explosion of light going out and filling you at every level of awareness and every level of being, completely bringing your vibration up to unconditional love. Every cell, every molecule, and all those spaces in between are filled with the joy, the passion, the intimacy, and the love of the divine masculine and the divine feminine.

**Anchor the Energy:** Pull that big white energy back into a column of light that extends from your heart up to Father Sky, 36 inches above your head, and extending from your heart down to the center of Mother Earth.

See it anchoring your energy, connecting through every single one of your chakras through your divine heart, divine masculine, divine feminine, Father Sky, and Mother Earth, so you are fully connected and know that this energy is available to you at every level of awareness and every level of being in every moment.

Feel the presence and connection to Mother Earth, and the inspiration from Father Sky and know that it flows through you in every moment. All you need to do is tap into your heart energy to access it.

## Invitation

I invite you to sit and feel this connected and centered energy and come up with a physical symbol, to anchor in this energy so that whenever you want it, all you need to do is make the sign and it will remind your body energetically of your connection to divine masculine and divine feminine energy; to remind you that you are centered between heaven and earth, and your heart knows the answer.

I would love to hear how this meditation was for you. Email me your comments and observations carolyn@carolynmcgee.com.

For a recorded version and additional resources, visit: https://carolynmcgee.com/resources/

---

**Intuitive Coach & Teacher, Carolyn McGee, specializes in amplifying YOUR Intuitive Superpower to listen to, trust and follow your soul's path to living the most joyful, healthy, connected, abundant, and purposeful life. She has taught thousands of professional, corporate, and entrepreneurial women to trust themselves and their intuition so they can show up in their full power in business and life.**

**By showing you the way back to your intuition, she helps you enhance your ability to receive messages and understand your guidance**

24/7. Then you can take empowered action so that you release second-guessing for good, and you feel 100% confident in making crystal clear decisions.

With a background of 20+ years in High Tech, Carolyn knows firsthand the importance of living from a blend of her masculine and feminine energies. Her unique combination of Angel, Animal & Intuitive connection, EFT, Energy Healing and Ministry created her "*Soul Clarity System*" for powerful healing, heart-centered connection, and inspired action.

She has co-authored eight bestselling books, is a popular TV co-host and sought-after speaker and blogger. www.CarolynMcGee.com

Join her in her "Enhance Your Intuition" Facebook group: https://www.facebook.com/groups/EnhanceYourIntuition/

CHAPTER 8

# Self Awareness

## Reduce Stress with the Enneagram

BY GERISE M. PAPPAS, CPC

In 1975 my dad moved my family from Indian Lake, New Jersey to Baltimore, Maryland. At that time, I was a nine-year-old, fun-loving kid who enjoyed many friends, sleepovers, bike riding, and awesome adventures living in Indian Lake. Upon moving to Baltimore, I was eager to make new friends in fourth grade at my new school, but a very different reality greeted me. I didn't fit in. I spoke with a New Jersey accent. I had beautiful long hair, but my mom got tired of brushing it, so she had it cut short early in the school year. Puberty was beginning, and my hair got frizzy in Baltimore's humidity. My new classmates were not kind and started calling me, "Burr head" and "George Washington." My new classmates were rejecting me, and my light started going out.

That sinking feeling of self-doubt at nine years old is my first memory of experiencing the debilitating kind of doubt that can arise when type 6 is under stress. When I told my mom what happened in school, she responded, "It could be worse," and "Sticks and stones will break your bones, but names will never hurt you." But she was wrong. Words did hurt, and I was hurting. Type 6 thrives on connection, support, and constancy. Yet, I was not getting the emotional empathy and holding I needed as a nine-year-old type 6, from my mother or anyone. This basic need for emotional safety, security, and certainty was ripped out from underneath me in Baltimore that year. I didn't know who or what to trust for support, so I became withdrawn and cautious. Being ostracized catalyzed chronic self-doubt. After that, nothing went very well socially. I had lost my confidence and trust in myself. Doubting oneself can be a self-defeating strategy that type 6 uses to keep themselves safe. *If I withdraw and am careful, maybe I can avoid being harmed.* The fun-loving kid I knew myself to be at Indian Lake was gone. I began to wonder if I would ever find her again.

In 2007 a friend invited me to attend a small gathering to learn about the Enneagram. As I sat listening to the teacher, I found myself suddenly challenging him. The teacher responded to me, saying, "You are counter-phobic as heck." Being counter-phobic is when you deny fear and simultaneously take risks to prove to yourself that you're stronger than fear itself. I was taken aback by this teacher's bluntness, but I knew he was right. I had just received a wake-up call that was about to mean something very significant for my evolution. They say *when the student is ready, the teacher appears.* The Enneagram was about to become one of my greatest teachers.

Unknown sources of stress within me started to reveal themselves. I began to become aware of the ways I showed up in life that were false fronts of confidence, boldness, and strength. I realized these masks of defense developed as a form of protection to keep myself and others safe from harm. For the first time, I could also see with compassion that I had constructed a wall of protection around my heart. With awareness, this wall started to crumble, and something new began to emerge.

A feeling of tenderness started to arise from within me; a very vulnerable and even terrified part of me dared to come forth. I could feel myself soften and see that others were there to support me. The part of me that worried about others' intentions and how they might react to me started to relax. All of this was uncomfortable to feel, but I soon recognized these were precious parts of me that had been longing for my love and attention.

I was drawn to read *The Sacred Enneagram* by Christopher Heuertz and learned about the fundamental, core need of my type 6 personality, which is the need to be sure, certain, or secure. At first, understanding how my personality created strategies to meet this need was not obvious. As I looked deeper and did inner work around this need, I had illuminating "aha" moments. While the need to be sure, certain, or secure can serve many basic positive purposes, I started seeing how my inner type 6 tends to get over-focused and fixated on this need to survive and avoid being harmed. When I'm gripped by this need or identified with it, it's like I'm in a fearful scarcity trance and cut off from my inner guidance and wisdom. In addition, I discovered that this trance keeps me from recognizing my strategies and deeper motivations. When this happens, I'm skeptical about others' intentions and ambivalent to love. Even worse, I project my doubts and fears onto others.

While seeing all of this wasn't fun, it was my doorway to freedom and empowerment. My daily practice started to help me catch when I was over-focused on this need. I began to notice how this need shows up in my mind as doubt or fear and in my body as tension, like breathing shallowly, a knot in my stomach, or tight shoulders. With this awareness, I could make a new choice: to focus my attention in a more healthy and productive way.

Through the lens of the Enneagram, I began to see my life newly and with great compassion. This included seeing my deeper motivations and blind spots caused by strategies that I used to get my core needs met. Most importantly, I started accessing inner resources that opened me to unprecedented self-love and fulfillment. Self-knowledge is the source of empowerment. The Enneagram offers a highly specific map for understanding ourselves and others.

The Enneagram is a whole-person integrated system for healing, growth, and transformation. Understanding and applying this system is a highly effective and heart-centered approach for addressing the doubt, fear, and anxiety that are at an all-time high in our lives, society, and media. When experienced chronically, these emotions are a tremendous source of disease and stress. In this context, when one truly understands how the Enneagram type 6 specifically works within each of us, it becomes a powerful portal for self-awareness and connection. This gives you the tools to access your inner guidance and wisdom, no matter what is happening.

Living inside each of us is the magnificent growth potential of the awakened type 6, as well as the possibility for doubt and fear, which creates separation within ourselves and our relationships. Whether your core Enneagram type is 6 or another type, it is important to understand that type 6's core need to be sure, certain, or secure are also basic human needs. How this need shows up in types other than 6 will vary and look different depending on your type. Learning how to work powerfully with these needs when they get triggered can reduce a tremendous amount of stress in our lives.

As a part of my practice for type 6, the Enneagram showed me that the true strength of my heart comes forth when I am being courageous. This courage is not about me being brave. This kind of courage asks me to "meet myself" by bringing kind attention, awareness, breath, and love to all aspects of me, especially the fearful, anxious, angry, disappointed, hurt, and heartbroken parts.

This courage is a quality of presence; it has the power to transform stress, anxiety, and fear into a state of calm and grounded presence that reconnects us to our inner guidance, wisdom, and knowing.

From practicing the self-awareness techniques and working with masterful teachers and coaches, a sustainable transformation has taken root inside of me. I won't kid you; it takes practice, willingness, and courage. However, true empowerment comes from "catching yourself," while your strategy to fulfill your core need tries to take you down a "rabbit hole"!

## Technique Overview

The idea here is to understand your unconscious sources of stress. By looking within and getting to know how your core need drives your personality, you can take your power back in ways you can't even imagine right now. You can benefit from engaging in the practices below, whether you know your Enneagram type or not.

The following Enneagram-based practices are designed to shift your conscious state from being stressed to centered and grounded. With the Enneagram, we do this by aligning our three Centers of Intelligence: the Head Center, the Heart Center, and the Belly Center. Within each of these centers arise three Enneagram types or portals of healing. While one type is our home base, which has its particular growth path and challenges, the healing energetic gifts for each of the nine Enneagram types live inside all of us.

You don't need to do the work for every type. Use the list below as a menu and consider it a list of options for discovering the possibilities for healing inside you.

The core need inquiry process is an opportunity to get in touch with unconscious sources of stress, illuminate blind spots within you, and open you to new possibilities for living. If you would like to discover your type or would like coaching around your type, go to GerisePappas.com for more information.

## Fundamental Core Need of Each Enneagram Type

### BELLY TYPES:

Type 8—The need to be against
Type 9—The need to avoid
Type 1—The need to be perfect

### HEART TYPES:

Type 2—The need to be needed
Type 3—The need to succeed
Type 4—The need to be unique or special

### HEAD TYPES:

Type 5—The need to perceive or understand
Type 6—The need to be sure, certain or secure
Type 7—The need to avoid pain

The Enneagram-based practices below guide you to consciously become more curious about parts of yourself that have been hidden. Existing defense mechanisms and survival strategies get in the way of being whole and healthy. Each type develops strategies around their core need. Understanding the origin of your own strategies will help you discover whether they are facilitating your growth or keeping you stuck. When you discover what triggers your strategies, you create opportunities to make new choices. For example, if I'm doubting myself, catch myself doing it, say to myself, *Hey, stop that, trust yourself,* and then begin again from a more grounded and centered state, that's powerful.

Each type is a portal of self-awareness. If you know your type, I would recommend doing the practices for that one first. There is value in doing the practice for any type to which you are drawn. If you are new to the Enneagram, this inquiry may assist you in discovering your type. Given that the need for security and certainty is relevant for our times and that my personal story conveys what happens when type 6 experiences stress, I have provided an inquiry into the core need for type 6 below.

To access the inquiries for all nine Enneagram types, go to GerisePappas.com/Resources.

## Journaling Guidelines for the Core Need Inquiry

- Answer these questions without editing. Let your stream of consciousness flow.
- When nothing more comes, ask the question again and see if more ideas come.
- Write with as much detail as possible.
- Notice sensations that arise in your body as you reflect on your responses.
- Bring your breath to any sensations that you notice in your body.
- Don't force anything. You can't do this incorrectly.
- Stay with yourself with kindness and gentleness, and allow what is.

- Tell any inner critics that they are "off duty." This is a non-judgment zone.
- Be curious and open to receive your inner wisdom.
- Look within through the lenses of curiosity, kindness, and compassion.

## Core Need Inquiry for Type 6

*Core need for type 6 is "to be sure, certain, or secure":* This need has to do with how we keep ourselves safe. One way the type 6 in us does this is by keeping doubt from arising. Finding things to be certain about can be a way that we create a feeling of security, and by keeping self-doubt at bay, we alleviate anxiety. When the type 6 in us loses faith or becomes skeptical, it can cause us to scramble for certainty or security. Rather than looking within, the type 6 strategy tends to defer to an authority outside of ourselves for guidance and certainty. The authority can be people or systems.

### *JOURNALING QUESTIONS*

- How does the need to be sure, certain, or secure show up in my relationships, work, and experience of living in general?
- How does overfocusing on this need create anxiety, deplete my energy, or impair my productivity?
- If I had faith that what I needed will be there when I need it, how would that ease my anxiety?

## The Antidote to Stress for Type 6

Courage is the transformational quality of the heart that allows us to show up fully in the moment for whatever needs our attention. When we are fully present and courageous, our intuition is operating at its peak, and we simply *know* what to do. We are grounded and paying attention to what life is presenting to us in each moment. We are one with our inner guidance. Being courageous is not about being brave. Courageousness is the ability to tune in and "meet ourselves" exactly as we are, with whatever feelings are arising, and do what needs to be done.

## *JOURNALING QUESTIONS*

- What could become possible if I brought the quality of courage or courageousness to something in my life that is causing me stress?
- By imagining this new possibility and being courageous, how does this change how I feel inside?

---

**As humans, we all have doubts, conflicting feelings, and unfulfilled needs at times. We may find ourselves getting stuck in destructive thought and behavior patterns and get caught unaware. As a Certified Professional Coach and Enneagram Specialist, Gerise Pappas empowers growth-oriented individuals to honor the hidden parts of themselves so they can change these patterns with confidence and courage. Her empathy, intuition, and gentle, moment-to-moment observations create a safe space that increases clients' self-awareness and unleashes the power to consciously change their lives. As part of her transformational coaching practice, Gerise offers Enneagram typing sessions, one-to-one coaching, as well as Enneagram classes and workshops. Additionally, as an inspirational speaker, she enjoys enthusiastically sharing the lessons she has learned through her deep, multi-faceted healing journey, and over twenty years of coaching.**

**In the words of one of her clients, "If you want to understand the underpinnings of what motivates you, look no further than working with this wonderful, warm, talented woman." Uncovering core needs and motivations allows clients to make many more conscious choices in their everyday lives, leading to reduced stress, improved relationships, and increased self-knowledge. The power of her Enneagram-based discovery process, extensive Enneagram knowledge, and transformational coaching approaches enable clients to let go of habits that no longer serve them. Her discovery questions and "loving mirror" observations facilitate deeper revelations necessary for lasting change.**

During her time in California, Gerise studied various forms of meditation, mindfulness, and other integrative modalities. Her studies with the Enneagram began in 1996. Highly respected Enneagram teachers that Gerise has been fortunate to study with include Helen Palmer, Russ Hudson, Jessica Dibb, Beatrice Chestnut, Uranio Paes, and Andrea Isaacs. Her authentic empathy with her clients stems from her own relentless willingness to use the Enneagram system, self-awareness practices, and coaching modalities to integrate abandoned and forgotten parts of herself. Her journey and background have positioned her to help others "re-parent" themselves the way she has, facilitating emotional healing from a place of power and permission.

If you would like to further explore any insights that you had from the Core Need Inquiries or discover more about your Enneagram type, go to GerisePappas.com.

# CHAPTER 9
# Guided Imagery
## Using Visualization to Heal
### BY DR. JOYCE FISHEL, PT, DPT

"There's a big, furry, striped animal in this tree with us. It's a tiger, run!"

I still vividly remember how my friends and I would laugh hysterically as we slapped at mosquitoes, jumped, swam, climbed, crawled, and ran through the jungle along with Ernie on his tiger hunt on the LP, *Having fun with Ernie and Bert – Tiger Hunt* (1972). I must've played that album a million times, and to this day, I can still hear the squeaks of his "trusty, rusty telescope."

Even now, so many years later, I still remember the excitement and giddiness I felt while listening to *Tiger Hunt,* and it automatically brings a smile to my face every time. I can picture the scene in my mind and *feel* it in my body.

Children are naturally gifted with imagination and the ability to creatively play. Looking back now, I realize that the *Tiger Hunt* is a form of guided imagery.

Like many children growing up in the '70s, my parents encouraged my imagination so I would entertain myself. Well, *encouraged* might not be the right word. That's just the way it was. I grew up as an only child in rural Nebraska with parents who were quite old-fashioned by today's standards. My mom was a proud housewife who kept the household in order. She had an uncanny talent for playing music by ear. She also hated getting dirt under her nails and so often left me to play alone outside. My father worked long hours outdoors as a roughneck. He was an oil field foreman who was just too plain tired to do anything after working a full day of physical labor. My job was to be a kid and do what kids do best. "Go play."

If my friends couldn't come out to play, then I played by myself. Spending countless hours alone, I learned early on how to quell any feelings of loneliness in the landscape of my imagination. I excavated under rocks and bushes for new species of creepy-crawlies. I read books, recreated the storylines with my dolls, and snapped polaroids to capture their adventures. When I got bored, I would lay on the grass in my yard, staring up at the sky, watching clouds shapeshift, or close my eyes and watch patterns of light dance upon my eyelids. If I gently pressed around the roundness of my eyeballs, my fingerprints would miraculously light up, and new patterns would emerge. I entertained myself with magical patterns that only I could see. Eventually, I would be filled with the urge to get my colors or paints and recreate these vivid imaginations on paper.

As I grew older, reality started to replace my imagination, gradually morphing into worry and anxiety. I was praised for my creativity in art class while at the same time being teased by teachers and friends for my "overactive imagination."

"Stop acting like your weird self," my best friend would tell me. So, I did my best to fit in and do what I imagined it meant to be normal. My imagination soon began fueling my fears, and anxiety triggered a reaction in my gut that felt like a swarm of grasshoppers swooping through my insides. It's probably little wonder that I was put on medication for a nervous stomach at the age of 12 and had an eating disorder by the age of 14. I had unintentionally learned how to use my imagination to scare myself, and it affected me physically.

My imagination had become both my gift and my curse.

It took me many years to better understand that my weakness was also a source of strength. I learned how to use the power of guided imagery to heal my stress and anxiety.

It turns out our brains don't differentiate between our thoughts and our real actions. The mind and body are wired to make it feel like you are experiencing something simply by thinking about it. The same neural pathways are stimulated whether you perform a real action or just think about performing that action.

Thoughts and emotions affect our physiology resulting in changes in body temperature, organ function, and physical control. Good examples of this are when you get "the tingles" while thinking about someone who turns you on, or when you feel your heart pounding in your chest while thinking about speaking in public.

Research shows that positive mental imagery can improve physical health and mental health by reducing stress, lowering blood pressure, alleviating pain, and even improving athletic performance. Guided imagery can be used anywhere, anytime, to gain these benefits.

Although guided imagery is sometimes referred to as visualization, it is experienced in the whole body, not just mentally. Guided imagery is more effective when it combines all the senses: sight, sound, smell, taste, touch, and kinesthetic: the feeling of position and movement of your body.

## How to Create Your Own Guided Imagery Script

### CHOOSE YOUR INTENTION

For imagery to be most effective, you need to decide upon a specific goal. For example, perhaps you want to alleviate pain, decrease stress or anxiety, boost confidence, or improve athletic performance.

## KEEP IT SIMPLE

When first learning to use guided imagery, begin by practicing something familiar. For example, ease anxiety or stress by imagining a scene that is peaceful and calm, or imagining how a perfect dive feels as you slice into the water moments before you dive in.

## EXPERIMENT WITH PERSPECTIVE

You can use an internal or external perspective. Internal perspective is when you do an activity and imagine it happening to you through your own eyes. External perspective is when it's as if you're watching yourself in a video. It may be helpful to experiment with different perspectives to see which you prefer. The most important thing to consider is that you're able to both see and feel the images you create regardless of the perspective you choose.

## WRITE IT DOWN

Once you determine your goal and which perspective you prefer, you can start writing your own imagery script to fit your own needs. Consider recording your script so that you aren't distracted by having to read it. You will then be able to listen anytime, anywhere.

Below are examples of simple imagery scripts to get you started. Imagine yourself fully immersed in each situation and allow yourself to experience any emotions or feelings that may come up. If your mind wanders or goes to a negative place, pause the imagery, and return to the breath.

## GUIDED IMAGERY I:

- Find a familiar object in the room and get into a comfortable position: standing or sitting with both feet flat on the ground.
- Next, take a few slow breaths. Breathe into your belly and relax your body with each exhale.
- Observe the object you have selected. Focus on every detail.

What is its shape, color, texture, weight?

- Now, close your eyes. Imagine the object with your mind's eye. Focus on all the details. Can you imagine how it feels? Its weight, shape, and texture? Can you imagine if it feels cool or warm to the touch?
- Open your eyes and compare your image with the real object.
- Close your eyes and imagine the details again.
- Take two or three more relaxing breaths and slowly open your eyes.

## GUIDED IMAGERY II:

- Find a comfortable position: standing, sitting, or lying down.
- Start by taking a few slow breaths. Breathe into your belly and let your body relax more with each exhale.
- Close your eyes and take two or three more deep breaths while continuing to relax your body.
- Squeeze your hands into fists tightly and notice how your hands and forearms feel. Notice the tension in the muscles of your arms and hands. Feel your fingers pressing against your palm.
- Now, relax your hands. Can you feel your muscles relax? Imagine how the sensations in your forearms and hands felt when you were squeezing your fists? Can you feel the position of your arms and hands?
- Take two or three more relaxing breaths and slowly open your eyes.

## GUIDED IMAGERY III

- Find a comfortable position: standing, sitting, or lying down.
- Start by taking a few slow breaths. Breathe into your belly and relax more with each exhale.
- Close your eyes and take two or three more deep breaths. Feel your body releasing tension with each exhale.

- Imagine you are standing on the sidewalk outside of your house or apartment.
- In your mind, imagine the building and all its details: the colors, the texture of the walls, the windows, and door. What time of year is it? Summer, spring, fall, or winter?
- Walk to the front door and notice how it appears larger as you get closer. Do you hear your footsteps?
- Reach out and put your hand on the door handle. Feel the shape and temperature of the handle in your hand as you turn it. Open the door and notice what you feel as you step inside.
- Walk through your house to your kitchen. See the colors of the walls, the countertops, sink, stove, windows, and floor.
- Notice all the details as you look around your kitchen. What do you feel? Can you imagine the lingering aroma of a cooked meal or coffee?
- Now, turn around and walk back through your home to the front door.
- Place your hand on the door handle, and walk out. What is the weather like? Can you feel it? Notice if you feel sunshine or a breeze on your skin.
- Take two or three more relaxing breaths and slowly open your eyes.

Visit https://www.bluelotusphysicaltherapy.com/resources to download a guided imaging recording I have created for anxiety and pain relief.

---

**Joyce Fishel is a holistic physical therapist, artist, and educator living in Baltimore, Maryland. She considers herself an eternal student of life. After earning a bachelor's degree in Fine Art in painting and sculpture at the University of Nebraska—Lincoln, she realized that her true passion is in teaching the art of human anatomy and empowering people to move past chronic pain.**

**Since receiving a Doctorate degree in physical therapy, she has continued to educate her patients and other healthcare providers techniques to improve movement and pain management using the mind-body approach to wellness.**

**She currently owns her own private practice specializing in visceral manipulation and movement education. In her spare time, she enjoys eating dark chocolate, traveling, theater, and puppets.**

**www.BlueLotusPhysicalTherapy.com**

CHAPTER 10

# Mindful Eating

## Using Food as Medicine

BY HEMALI VORA, MPT,
JFB MFR PRACTITIONER

## My Story

The year was 2014. What looked like another typical day at work had something special stored for me. My schedule was packed; I was going to see eight Physical Therapy patients that day. As I walked into my patient's room with a clipboard in one hand and a walker in the other, a surgeon came in behind me. Little did I know what I would hear "that day" would change me. The surgeon said, "Hello Mr. Smith, I have good & bad news for you. The good news is that I can save your leg, but the bad news is that we will have to amputate your left foot. The foot is very necrotic and cannot be salvaged. We'll need to do this surgery immediately."

The patient was speechless; I could sense his mind racing with questions but could not articulate it. I had a few too. I thought to myself, *why do people wait so long? Why didn't he do anything about his foot before this? Where was his family, and why didn't they help him? Why do people wait to change until a crisis occurs? Why not proactively make their health a priority?*

I was emotional, frustrated, and a bit angry, as though I was going through the grieving process for the patient. That afternoon, as the rehab team gathered for lunch and charting, I asked the questions that were on repeat in my head. As I was talking, something clicked, and I listened to myself, feeling like a hypocrite. I realized I needed to take a good look at myself and evaluate what I was doing to my kids.

My kids have severe asthma, allergies, and sensitivities to foods, things their primary care nor the allergist could figure out. This means we were "frequent flyers" in the pediatrician's office. My daughter struggled with acid reflux since she was a month old. We did numerous tests, and she was misdiagnosed a few times, which resulted in hospitalization and continued tests. We kept giving her medicines to manage the symptoms. Then came asthma. We couldn't figure out the triggers for acute episodes. And testing was limited to the general American diet. We were giving her steroids to mask the symptoms. I knew what steroids would do to her body. She was developing a round face, weight gain, painful bones, and low immunity.

Then my son, who initially had seasonal allergies, started having acute asthma attacks. His attacks were unpredictable. Initially, nobody could figure out the cause of his allergies or sensitivities, either. Along with a sensitivity to some food colorings, preservatives, pesticides, yeast, and grass, he had "Emotional Asthma." He would have an attack from simply laughing or crying too much. There were times when we had to control his emotions. The kids couldn't play on the grass or participate in any sports activities.

With traditional medicines failing us, I knew I had to focus on alternative therapies. I grew up in India, around people practicing varied ancient therapeutic modalities. Things like Ayurveda, yoga, meditation, kriya, acupressure, acupuncture, Reiki, prayers, chanting, sounds, incense, and using herbs and spices as medicine were a way of life for my parents, grandparents, aunts, cousins, and neighbors. These things were part of me. I grew up knowing you can heal your body by nourishing it with sattvic foods, herbs, and spices. I was taught you can heal your body by nourishing your mind with your thoughts, what you hear, and the words you speak and listen to. I know you can heal your body by nourishing your soul with meditation, breathwork, prayers, chanting, music, and dancing. I know you can heal your body by nourishing your emotions with sounds, aromas, and your feelings. Above all, I know you can heal your life by staying connected to nature, in its purest forms, and by doing "Seva" (selfless service to others).

But along the way, after moving to America, we slowly adapted to a new culture and way of life, including fast foods. My parents maintained our Indian traditions and culture, but my siblings and I went out to explore the world, and some of the old ways of life took a backseat.

Once I got married, we maintained a vegetarian, sattvic diet. But in those days, we ate out two or three times a week. I started cooking at home more once I had kids. Even with full-time work, I was able to nurse both my kids for a year and even made their baby food at home. My family supported me. I tried to stay away from allergens as much as possible. But, when the kids started elementary school, they wanted to eat foods their friends ate in class parties, which were colored and loaded with sugar. That made them sick more and more. Even the homemade herbal tinctures and remedies my mom came up with didn't help much.

I became stressed and tired of constant illnesses, coughing, vomiting, and sleepless nights. I couldn't work a regular job anymore because I needed days off when the kids were sick, so I started working PRN as a therapist at a hospital close to home. Work was unstable and inconsistent. We took a big financial hit and had big healthcare bills. There were times we lived paycheck to paycheck. I, too, started getting sick, gained weight, and suffered from systemic inflammation. I built up and stored a lifetime of resentment, anger, guilt, frustration, and shame. I was ready to explode.

I believe we are more than equipped to deal with obstacles in life. And if we can't take care of it ourselves, the Universe/God/Divine sends angels in the form of people into our lives to support us. I had my own angels around me, guiding me. My husband, parents, and siblings were always there to help. But as things crumbled around me, my emotions were out of control. I couldn't take care of my family as I'd hoped. I decided to invest in and take care of myself first, so I could take care of them. My first stint with healing started when I enrolled in the Art of Living class. The techniques I learned stabilized and balanced my emotions, and things started shifting. Then Reiki found me, and I became a Reiki Master teacher, level I and II certified, which brought more clarity, stability, and balance. I was able to help my kids calm down and to lessen their symptoms.

Meanwhile, my friend Sarah Scholl, a physical therapist and an Integrative Nutrition Coach was encouraging me to make slow changes, including a more organic diet, adding vitamins and minerals, and eliminating foods that caused mucus. She helped me pay attention to the ingredients in different products. It took a few months of her coaching, followed by that incident in the hospital for me to really commit and say, "I'm *going to take responsibility for my and my family's health. We are going to spend money on us; on good food."*

At times you absolutely have to make use of conventional medicine, but I knew in my heart there was something better I could do to change our circumstances. I always kept an open mind and believed there were many solutions to being healthy and well. I enrolled in an online Integrative Nutrition Program at IIN. With that knowledge, I started cooking more at home, ordering less take-out, and following more of a whole-food, plant-based diet. When I started on this journey, I went back to what I knew about food, herbs, and spices while growing up. My plan was to move away from processed foods with colors, artificial sweeteners, artificial flavors, and pesticides—even if it came from local farms. We started getting organic, non-GMO produce, and products. We threw away everything, including shampoos, toothpaste, deodorants, household cleaning products, laundry detergent, and vitamins filled with chemicals and colors. I incorporated green smoothies, using more alkaline ingredients, antioxidants, microgreens, and immune-boosting produce. The transformation of introducing more greens, different vegetables, fresh fruits, and even roots and herbs started to yield results. We felt more energetic, our vital signs improved, and my kid's visits to doctors reduced significantly.

It was a major lifestyle change, and I'm so glad we did it. Getting here wasn't easy. There were angry outbursts, crying, fights, and falling back to old ways of eating. Sometimes, it was one step forward and ten steps back. But we picked up and moved forward. It took us a year to get a grip on all the changes. As the kids get older, we are continually evolving. Does this mean I don't let my kids indulge in some mouth-watering pizza or fries? No, but they are now aware of its effects and ask for less of those kinds of foods. And while clean eating is one aspect of the puzzle, you still need to continue with your daily exercise, meditation, and breathing techniques.

Personally, I started following more of an intuitive and mindful way of nourishing my body, mind, and spirit, asking questions like, *what would you like to eat? What is it that you need today to nourish you, to feel happy?* I started being more in the present and listening to my body's GPS system; it's wants and needs. I asked myself, *why am I craving this? Is it to feed the inflammation or to nourish the body? Do I feel bloated, gassy, sleepy, or focused, energized after a meal?* I started being kind and compassionate towards my body, loving every bump and curve and even the fat cells. While cooking, I would listen to uplifting music, prayers, or chanting, and started enjoying the whole process of cooking and eating. I gave food lots of love and good energy before it reached the table.

I hope this story awakens something in you. Wishing you love, light, and compassion to transition into better health and lifestyle. For recipes, you can visit www.hemalivora.com. Now, here is a beautiful exercise to get you started using mindfulness and mindful eating for your own health and wellness.

## Mindful Eating Exercise

Try to keep quiet during the exercise, without any distractions, with an open heart and a gentle curiosity. If you like, you can record these steps and listen to it while you do the exercise.

1. Grab a few nuts or pieces of fruit.

2. Set yourself up in a comfortable seated position on a chair or cushion on the floor. Take a moment to just be in that quiet space, sit up straight, open up your chest. Take a few deep breaths, relax your face, your shoulders, arms, and hands. Relax your stomach muscles, your legs, and your feet. Notice if any thoughts are running around in your head, any emotions or sensations. Then bring awareness back to your breathing, inhale, and exhale.

3. Bring your attention to the food in your hand and imagine you're seeing and eating it for the first time. Examine it with all of your senses. Look closely at the food, take a moment to describe it, what do you see? Examine the contours, the folds, the rims, the colors, shape, and size.

4. Imagine what it took for this food to get to your hands: sunshine, water, time, processing, and shipping. You can give gratitude to everyone involved in the cultivation and preparation of this food. You may do your own gratitude or spiritual blessings.

5. Now place the food between your fingers. How does it feel in your hand? Smooth, sticky. Move it around with your fingers and really get a sense of its texture, temperature, mass, ridges, and weight.

6. Now bring the food close to your nose and take a deep breath, does it have a smell? What does it smell like? Notice if you have any memories, sensations, or reactions in your body.

7. Bring the food up to your ears, if you move it between your fingers, do you hear anything? What do you hear? Do you feel its energy?

8. Now close your eyes and put the food against your lips. What thoughts cross your mind? Likes or dislikes for that food item. Now

put the item in your mouth but don't chew it or bite it just yet. Roll it against your tongue and notice if you can taste it before you bite it. See how it feels inside your mouth? How does your body respond?

9. Put the food between your teeth but don't bite it. Notice any saliva in your mouth. Now position it in a way that you can just take one bite. Bite it and feel the burst of flavor. What does it taste like? Can you describe it?

10. Take another bite of it, but don't swallow it yet. Roll that flavor against your tongue. What did that feel like or taste like? Then very slowly begin chewing it as many times as possible and notice parts of your mouth that are involved in chewing. Notice the sound and movement of chewing as you continue to notice sensations and flavor.

11. As you get ready to swallow the food, notice the experience of any sensation or impulse to swallow. What's that like? Swallow it when you're ready and notice the point of swallowing when you can no longer feel the food going down the back of your throat or any feeling as it makes its way down to your stomach.

12. Notice any tastes or sensations that linger. Be aware of reactions in your body and in your mouth. Be aware that your body has taken in the weight and food energy of that nut or fruit.

13. Now simply be aware for a few moments; of your breath, your thoughts, feelings, sensations in your mouth, and in your body. Bring your awareness back to your breath. Inhale and exhale a couple of times, and when you're ready, you can slowly open your eyes.

I understand it's not realistic to eat every meal in this manner. But we can surely take 20 minutes of our time for each meal. Before we eat, we can check in with ourselves and ask some questions:

What's my intention? Is my intention to eat slowly? Is it to add healthy food into my body to nourish my brain, nourish my body and my family? Sit down with your food, smell it, take a bite, and chew each bite about 20-25 times. Put your spoons or forks down, or if you eat with your hands, like me, just stop for 20-30 seconds and take a couple of deep breaths in between the bites.

Let's have a relationship with food and be mindful of how it affects our body, mind, and spirit. Eat food intentionally, truly savoring the food, and paying close attention, just like a sommelier (wine taster). Attention to food is sensory-driven; what we see, hear, touch, taste, feel, and smell. It's about if we're hungry, thirsty, angry, anxious, or confused. Slowing down and listening to our bodies and doing one thing at a time is important. Making a small ritual to consider all that goes into our meal will help bring mindfulness to your life. This exercise puts pause into practice and also helps us cultivate pleasure, satisfaction, and gratitude...all from a morsel of food.

---

**Hemali V. Vora, MPT, is an owner and practitioner of Hemali Vora, Health and Wellness, LLC. She lives in Maryland and works in the DMV area. She is an expert medical intuitive healer with psychic gifts, an empath, and a spiritual advisor, who will teach you to tap into the powers that lie within you.**

**Her purpose in this lifetime is to guide you towards radical self-care, unconditional love, and compassion for self and inner peace. Having gone through her own journey filled with weight struggles, health challenges, healing crisis, and spiritual awakening, Hemali has learned the power of intuition and our body's potential to heal itself through nourishing its body, mind, emotion, and spirit. According to her, nutrition, energy, and spiritual work play a vital role in healing dis-ease and dis-harmony in your body.**

**Over two decades of working in healthcare as a PT, Myofascial Release practitioner, healer, and an educator, she has helped and guided hundreds of patients, clients and their families with chronic illnesses, disabilities, personal traumas, and in their spiritual journeys. She is**

**known to skillfully integrate ancient wisdom and modern science in her work.**

**Hemali teaches Level I, II, Master, and Karuna Reiki certification courses and cooking classes. She offers one-on-one or group sessions in her office, in your home and/or online distant healing sessions. You can reach her: 240-354-0129, www.hemalivora.com, www.facebook.com/coachhemali**

CHAPTER 11

# Tapping

## Easing Difficult Emotions

BY LAURA KNAPP MAZZOTTA, LCSW-R

For many years prior to my healing journey, I felt trapped within myself and my past. I wondered if I would always feel a sense of emptiness, resentment, and restlessness. I went to therapy for many years, but my mind and heart were still plagued with obsessive anxiety. Thank goodness for energy healing, which swooped in and dragged my ass out.

## My Healing Journey

When my parents got divorced (at age seven), I went to see a therapist for the first time. He was gentle, kind, and held such a compassionate space for me. The safety of his office was something I was yearning for, without even knowing it. I wanted to provide this space for others and help them heal, just as he helped me.

I've now been a successful therapist for over 16 years. I have helped countless clients with their healing and transformation. However, it wasn't until I got dangerously ill that I learned how to heal on a much deeper level.

Four years ago, I was hospitalized with sepsis. My fever went from 99F to 105F in 35 minutes. I was shaking violently, couldn't stand, and was incredibly disoriented. I had my first ambulance ride, and when I arrived, the nurse said, "What took you so long to call 911? If you had waited thirty minutes more, I don't know if we could have done anything for you."

I've never been so terrified. The months after hospitalization were even scarier. I went back to the hospital via ambulance several times. I could hardly stand and was dizzy for a solid three years. However, when a neurologist told me, "This is degenerative, and you're only going to get worse," I didn't believe him.

I just didn't see my future as degenerative. This was a culmination of several specialist visits with differing opinions. One of my favorites was the assessment of my relentless, stabbing ear pain. Doctor number one said I was grinding my teeth, and the other said, "There's a strong possibility that you have lymphoma," and "You need a CT scan right away."

## Finding the Lesson

As frustrating as all of this became, each of these events was an opportunity. I was motivated and encouraged to explore alternative ways to heal myself. I *knew* I was a spunky, playful soul with a lot ahead of me in this world. I couldn't sit back and wait for this supposedly inevitable sentence to unfold.

I was now determined, so I experimented with a host of healing modalities. Some worked. Some didn't. Ultimately, I knew it was up to *me* to decide which way to go—what a scary concept when I still felt so fragile.

I grew up listening to my elders, especially those in positions of authority, like doctors, nurses, and teachers. Now I was to pave my own path and listen to my internal wisdom, even when it opposed doctors' orders. This was uncharted territory. My good-girl persona was being challenged.

I was breaking out of the box, and guess what? It felt *freeing.* I felt enlivened and invigorated for the first time in a long time. The best part was the emotional change that naturally unfolded. I have truly *never* been as confident, decisive, and laid back as I am now.

Why? I learned to stop rejecting those parts of me I judged for so long, and appreciate them as lessons, as part of the unique tapestry that is me. I learned to release them in the form they were in (as emotions, memories, or physical sensations) and integrate them into new forms and belief systems.

## Tapping/EFT (Emotional Freedom Technique)

During my healing process, there were several effective tools I tried, but tapping/EFT was one of the most powerful. I'd used it with clients but never thoroughly explored or used it for myself. By the time I practiced EFT, my mind and body were restless, trying to figure out what was going on with me. I needed a tool that attended to both the mind and body.

Tapping/EFT is an energy psychology technique, created by Gary Craig and Roger Callahan, that involves tapping on certain acupressure points of the body while speaking statements of release and affirmation out loud.

By the age of seven, children have already developed their subconscious belief systems. These beliefs remain in the background, driving much of our interaction and experience in the world. We aren't consciously aware of their impact until we start developing physical or emotional symptoms.

As adults, addressing our subconscious beliefs raises self-awareness, and empowers us to choose new beliefs in alignment with who we want to become. If you've been experiencing repeating patterns, cycles, scenarios, physical symptoms, or negative emotions, it would be a good idea to explore tapping.

The goal of EFT is to release negative emotions and beliefs. This is an important first step to instilling healthier, more supportive belief systems.

Your mind and body are more receptive to new belief systems when you complete multiple rounds of tapping. The more rounds you do, the deeper the healing goes.

It is my belief that there is an emotional or energetic underpinning for all physical and mental illness. I was initially resistant to that idea when it was first presented to me. Then I learned from my own experience when recovering from sepsis.

If you're reading this guide to self-healing, you are looking for relief for some area of discomfort. Regardless of what this is for you, tapping can help on a mental, physical, emotional, and energetic level.

What could be more empowering than shifting your terrifying, horrific, and uncomfortable situations into working *for you*r greatest good? Especially when you are acting as your own transformational tool as you're tapping.

Are you ready to get started?

## How to Tap

Tapping/EFT operates by accessing the body's primary energy meridian (a channel that runs along the length of the spine) through tapping points. Just as the respiratory system distributes and operates the breath, the energy meridian circulates the body's energy.

The tapping points used to access this meridian are:

- The karate chop point (outside edge of the hand, between the end of the pinky finger and the wrist)
- Above the eyebrows
- The outside of the eye sockets
- Under the eyes
- Above the center of the top lip
- The center of the chin
- Just below each collarbone
- About four inches below each armpit
- Tapping the insides of each wrist together (some practitioners don't use this one)
- The top and center of the head

You'll find a chart with all of these points at:https://www.theakashictherapist.com/about-tapping-eft-emotional-freedom-technique.

When tapping starts, we open the sequence with a balanced statement that combines what you want to release with a statement of affirmation. There will be an example of this later. This statement should be spoken while tapping the karate chop point *only*. After reciting and tapping on this point a few times, we can move on to the rest of the exercise.

A sequence in EFT is comprised of moving through all of the points two times, the first while you're repeating statements of release and the second while you're repeating statements of affirmation. Sequences begin with tapping the karate chop point with one, two, three, or four fingers, whatever is most comfortable (the more, the better). You can apply as much pressure as you would like to feel the effects. You may want to take it easy when first starting out.

The first round of the sequence includes statements related to the *negative* emotion, energy, or symptom you want to release. It's important to identify a couple of these negative emotions before you tap, so you may want to write them down. Once you identify the negative emotion, or area you want to release, rate its severity on a scale of 1-10 (10 being the highest severity). This gives you a basis of comparison for when tapping is complete.

Sometimes it takes a few rounds of the release to feel ready to move on. After the release rounds of tapping are complete, the sequences of affirmations and new beliefs are spoken for each tapping point. Again, you may journal these beforehand if you can't come up with them as you're tapping. That way, you can read off of a written script if that's easier for you.

For video instructions for the following written example, please visit my resource page at: https://www.theakashictherapist.com/resources.

## Tapping in Action

Now you're ready to try this. Take three deep belly breaths, activating the parasympathetic nervous system and the relaxation response. Starting with the karate chop point, start tapping at the same time you make 2-3 of those balanced statements of release *and* affirmation.

For instance, the statement for the first point (karate chop) may be: "Even though I am furious right now, I completely love and accept myself." The second statement may be: "Even though I feel the heat rising in my body, I know this is a temporary sensation."

After making these first 2-3 statements, you move on to the sequences of tapping points listed above. These statements are going to describe the nature of what needs to be released.

For instance, moving onto the next tapping point (above the eyebrows), the statement could be: "All of this rage I have within me."

The next point (outside of the eyes) could be: "I just want to scream and yell from the rooftops." And so on, continuing through the tapping points until you reach the top of the head. You can keep going with another round of release statements if you don't feel ready to move on.

Since you've already started the release sequence with the karate chop point, you can skip it this time, and go right into statements of affirmation starting with the point above the eyebrow.

For instance (above the eyebrows): "I now choose to release all of this anger inside of me."

Next point (outside of the eyes): "I am aware of the control and compassion I have within."

Next point (Under the eyes): "I choose to send forgiveness and love to this situation."

And so on, until you've reached the final point at the top of your head. As in the initial rounds of releasing, multiple rounds of affirmations may be used.

Each full tapping sequence may bring up intense emotions or beliefs. Pay attention and journal about any statements that trigger you or resonate deeply. It will only deepen your understanding of the subconscious thoughts that have been revealed.

For a video module and workbook that explains how to create your own, personalized EFT script, please visit my website at: https://www.theakashictherapist.com/shop/creating-your-own-eft-script

## WHAT HAPPENS AFTER I TAP?

After an EFT cycle is complete, take a deep breath and tune into sensations in the body, mind, and emotional body. Rate yourself on that scale of 1-10 again. If distress remains, you can continue with additional tapping cycles.

You may feel like your body is buzzing after a tapping session. You will definitely feel more relaxed and have more mental clarity. To sustain this feeling, you can consistently repeat the affirmations from the tapping session or commit to tapping 1-3 times a day, depending on your level of dis-ease. If you don't feel any better, tap more, tap with fewer points, or tap with less pressure.

Having the attention of a personalized practitioner can also be helpful if you're struggling with tapping. A practitioner can help you process and determine the core issue, and provide support, comfort, and direction, so you feel safe as you're bringing up difficult feelings.

Being held in an unconditional space enhances the energy shift you can achieve through tapping. Allow someone to be your guide before you shy away from this practice. It's truly one of the most transformative therapeutic tools I have been blessed to experience.

Finally, make sure to drink a lot of water and remain aware of any energy shifts after EFT, like fatigue, thirst, or hunger. Take good care of yourself, as a nurse or loved one would care for you after medical treatment.

You are your own self-healer, which means empowering yourself through the strategies in this book and nurturing yourself with lots of tender, loving care. Energetically, you're already the person you want to become. You just need to tap into that core by peeling back layers of outdated conditioning. Become the version of you you've always desired. I promise that person is there waiting for you.

---

**Laura Mazzotta, LCSW-R, is an expert therapist, Certified Akashic Records Practitioner and Reiki Healer with over 16 years of experience. She guides therapists, coaches, and healers, with chronic dis-ease (negativity, anxiety, doubt, physical illness, or pain), to ease, energy and confidence in the space of the Akashic Records. With extensive knowledge and skills in modalities such as EFT (tapping), Regression Therapy, Trauma Work, and intuitive development, Laura knows how to guide your healing journey in a unique, powerful, and effective way.**

**During her recovery from a serious illness in 2016, Laura exhausted western medicine approaches and realized her deep passion for holistic methods, becoming an even greater advocate for personal development and healing. Laura knows true healing occurs much more powerfully when all components (physical, mental, energetic, and spiritual) of a person's issue are addressed. She's here to guide her clients in all steps on that journey.**

**Laura lives in New York, USA, with her husband and three children. She loves to read, travel, snuggle, and turn practically anything into a song. She also loves chocolate-covered strawberries. Chocolate lava cake isn't bad either.**

**You can find Laura at:**
**https://www.theakashictherapist.com/resources**

**Join her free Facebook group at:**
**https://www.facebook.com/groups/248267309861170 4/**

## CHAPTER 12

# Body Awareness

## Healing Through Somatic Experience

BY RAELIN SAINDON, B.S. PSY, RMT, C.HT.

Looking back at my beginnings and the route each experience guided me along, I can now see them through eyes and with a heart of love, forgiveness, compassion, and wonder at it all. This wasn't always my reality or my viewpoint. I, like so many, have had decades of upheaval, pain, suffering, and self-inflicted sabotage that kept me blaming, bitter, and victimized, purely by believing the stories I wallowed and imprisoned myself within.

I was always a curious and empathetic child; I came out questioning everything with an idealized view of everyone and the world around me. I *felt* the emotions, *heard* the thoughts, and *experienced* the pain and celebrations of others, particularly the adults in my world. I believed and saw the best in everyone, and perceived the true potential and deep-felt needs of others with uncanny accuracy. What I couldn't do was understand why most everyone around me didn't behave or see people and events this same way. It was this "essence" that invited some to manipulate and use me, and what I believed at the time, was to my detriment.

My early childhood experiences are peppered with trauma, neglect, and abuse on all levels; to include sexual abuse by my sister's father. My attachment to my parents was minimal and less than the ideal and loving norm. Growing up, I normalized most of my experiences, but the sexual abuse, in my mind, was flagged openly and honestly for what it was. It wasn't until I was in my mid 30's that I could genuinely see so much of my family dynamic for the breadth and depth of neglect and abuse it provided. Even now, mixed emotions rise within me and connect with my stomach, my heart, and my head. Being able to tune-in and learning to listen to my physical frame has saved me and given me the power of radical forgiveness and true release. More on that later.

The body truly remembers. We have often heard and perhaps said ourselves, *my body has its own mind.* Science and trauma-informed studies bear this to be true. In his seminal book, *The Body Keeps The Score: Brain, Mind, and Body in the Healing of Trauma*, psychiatrist and leading trauma expert, Bessel van der Kolk, M.D., shares that the mind-body connection is visceral and innate to our physical experiences. Rooted as a protectionary mechanism for survival, van der Kolk shares that even Charles Darwin noted and spoke of the physiological connections between the two: "Heart, guts, and brain communicate intimately via the pneumogastric nerve, the critical nerve involved in the expression and management of emotions in both humans and animals. When the mind is strongly excited, it instantly affects the state of the viscera; so that under excitement, there will be much mutual action and reaction between these, the two most important organs of the body." Bessel himself goes on to explain that, "If an organism is stuck in survival mode, its energies are focused on fighting off unseen enemies, which leaves no room for nurture, care, and love. For us humans, it means that as long as the mind is defending itself against invisible assaults, our closest bonds are threatened, along with our ability to imagine, plan, play, learn, and pay attention to other people's needs."

For me, the realization slowly became this: I cannot do for others what I don't know how to do for myself. I had always accepted and believed myself to be a giver, and that tending to others and looking after them was selfless and noble. I now know that I was simply bleeding my wounds onto my family, friends, and anyone that got close to me; and believed that fixing *them* was the true path to healing. This was my drug, my addiction, and a great distraction from the reality that followed me. Thinking I was the solution to their wounds, I was shown my own and just how deeply I was neglecting their care. We will always be drawn to the end of ourselves, the end of hiding, the end of deflecting, the end of self-destruction; the end of running. The beauty is that once we stop, catch, and slow our breath, we can begin to see, hear, and feel our lives with more clarity and connection than we ever knew existed. At that moment, our work begins.

Somatic connection, "mind-body awareness," is foundational to approaching healing holistically. The term *soma* is Greek for "living body," and *holistic*, contextually connects all systems to one another in their importance and expression. Somatic-experiencing has become a therapeutic technique that enables an individual to safely experience themselves and ultimately their life, through their mind-body-spirit reality. My healing began and continues in this way; and I lead others through this same process. It's important to understand that in experiences of high stress, pain, or trauma, the natural, built-in protection of our human existence is to disassociate or disconnect our mind from our physical body during such events. Our autonomic nervous system (ANS), is pre-programmed in this unique way to ensure our survival and quick reaction to physical and environmental threats. Experienced occasionally, this measure is self-regulating with the parasympathetic nervous system (PNS), acting as the "release and reset valve," and bringing the mind-body back online and functioning at its balance point.

Where this becomes an issue and creates problems is in chronic exposure to repeated threats, or when an event becomes "flagged," or highlighted so deeply in the mind, that a trigger-point is created. With any situation, thought, conversation, sight, smell, or other sensory experience that remotely resembles the original, our mind disconnects, and the body is sent into the stress response of fight-flight-freeze. All critical thinking stops, blood rushes to the vital organs, and we take off; either physically, mentally, or both. What often develops in this process once triggered, is the belief that we must be ever-vigilant, always on the lookout for any threat, and that it is not safe to be centered and calm within our body.

Somatic-experiencing reframes and rewires our physiology so that the mind-body-spirit connection is not only operating, but it is in harmony and unity at all times, regardless of external circumstances. In my self-practice as well as how I guide others through this, I begin with: thought awareness, guided physical self-touch, a standing meditation practice (as well as meditation in general), and focused mindful movement. I have witnessed lasting benefit, immediate physical-state shifts, increased self-soothing, and energy-clearing ability in my own life and in that of others. Reality shifts from fear, freeze, and flee to acceptance, allowing and embracing each moment as it is.

To begin, I invite you to notice your thought in this exact moment, as it is, no editing, no cleaning up the language, no rationalizing. Simply put, what *is* the thought as it exists; pure and unaltered? Write it down. Read it out loud to yourself. Say each word as though you are savoring a bite of a delicious dessert, tasting each syllable, chewing, and swallowing each morsel. Notice then, even in this description, is your mouth watering? Did you find yourself swallowing? Are you suddenly thirsty? Is your stomach growling? What physical sensations are rising as you read this or read your thought you wrote down? Does your breathing speed up from the chest; do you notice your hands or forehead are sweaty? Tune in. Notice. Write it down. Watch your hand as it forms the letters; feel the weight of it resting on the surface of the paper and how it glides across. How does the pen or pencil feel in your grasp; what position are your fingers in? Which hand is writing, and what is your non-dominant hand doing at the same time?

Shifting your focus and attending to what your body is experiencing is what thought awareness is all about. It begins with noticing; the exercise I just led you through is intentionally formatted with terms of sensory experience. The mind is merely a servant; in reality, it is *"The Us"* that lives within, guiding and directing while informing of its interpretation or giving meaning to an experience. Observing our thoughts with the language of physical sensation, builds, develops, and strengthens our mind-body connection.

Next, I invite you to place your hand/s on your body where you notice discomfort, heat/chill, tingling, numbness, or whatever physical sensation you observe. Guided physical self-touch involves placing our hands on an area of our body, which then communicates to the mind that something important is happening, and centers our mental energy there.

Remember when you were a child, and you fell, scrapped a knee, or jammed a finger? What did you instinctually do next? Yes, you held or touched that area of your body to ease pain; but this also was a strong, primal and energetic signal to your mind that *"something important is happening [here], send help!"* The mind takes notice and sends focused, intentional awareness and healing to those areas; all in a matter of nanoseconds. When we acknowledge our body sensations with touch, we are signaling to our mind and body to connect and provide cooperative healing to that location. Don't believe me? Watch what children do when they are hurt. They run to a parent or caregiver, offer the body part, and seek touch. A kiss. A hug. Being held. The simple act of laying your hands on where they hurt. The immediate outcome is connection, and often just as quickly as the pain or discomfort showed up, it is erased, and they return to their play all better. Guided physical self-touch re-minds us that our body is always communicating its needs and wants, which often reveal the why and where of our emotions.

In my Aikido practice, I was gifted with a standing meditation called Zhan Zhuang, [https://www.youtube.com/watch?v=1ednab-CIRhI] or *"Standing-on-Stake."* Five postures are flowed through in the morning, midday and evening, (the fifth posture is skipped at the evening period). The practice, as it's taught, has multiple benefits, primarily as a discipline to build one's qi (chi), or *"life-force energy."* I use it for all its benefits, but my primary focus in leading others through it is to entrain their mind to remain present within the body through the process. It is highly effective and intentional in every posture and body position. For me, my initial concern isn't the length of time that a client holds a posture, but more so, their physical observations that they sense while in a pose. Even the resistance or openness of the client to this practice is important feedback for me; knowing the progression of moving onto other techniques, or the need to go back to an earlier form. I encourage clients to stay focused upon one posture if they need deeper awareness and focused sensory experience. Connecting at their pace and level of safe-feeling is what I encourage. I also connect them to meditation, guided and silent. I invite you to enjoy this guided Chakra Meditation [https://www.youtube.com/watch?v=ues6UFd-7Ok] of mine.

Finally, focused and mindful movement can be found through dance, yoga, Tàijí (Tai Chi), Qi-gong, Barre-method, Pilates, or any other fluid and purposeful movement. I encourage clients toward those activities that connect movement with the body and positional awareness, concentration of a particular pose or stance, or focus upon a particular area, and whether it's relaxed or tense. In the beginning, to lay the foundation of this mind-body connection, it's important to slow things down and dial-in our level of concentration and create conscious movement. Listen to the tension in your neck, back, shoulders, or legs, softening in those areas with the thought of, *relax,* and breathing deeply.

Let's go through this together; bring your awareness to where you are at this moment as you're reading. Note the position of your body; seated or reclining. What do you feel/sense in your body? Tension? Numbness? Tiredness? Stand up or shift your position. Move your arms, your shoulders, and your neck. Relax and ease your jaw and your hips/back. Bring your awareness to your breathing. If you notice yourself breathing from the chest (stress-response breathing), take your hands and place one under the belly-button and the other over the belly-button and begin again. Inhale deep with the rising of your belly and exhale fully as it falls and is drawn to your back. Mindful movement creates opportunities for deeper awareness and connection of your mind with the body, all to focus concentration and create conscious movement.

In our human existence, we are gifted the opportunity to experience each moment fully and completely. It is our soul-contract and calling; what makes us uniquely human. For many of us, our experiences have taught us we are not safe within our physical frame. Through the healing gift of building a practice of Somatic-experience and connection, we can regain the wonder, awe, and joy of each moment that the mind-body-spirit trinity lovingly provides. We gain clarity, focus, and invite in new opportunities for growth and lasting change. We learn that we are safe, meet any challenge with ease and flow while remaining connected, centered, and present within our bodies. I invite you to begin exactly where you are, as you are, with a mind and body open to heal, change, grow, and love.

For more support in your healing, find resources here [https://raelinsaindon.com/resources/]. Namaste.

---

**Raelin Saindon, B.S Psy, RMT, C.Ht, is a Channel of WE are WE Consciousness, Spiritual Teacher & Healing Guide of The Healing Space. She is a Reiki Master Teacher, Certified Life Regressionist and Hypnotist, Certified Emotion Code & Ho'oponopono Practitioner and Quantum Healing student. Raelin holds a B.S. in Psychology with focused study and lived experience in Trauma, PTSD, and Inner Child Work. She teaches and guides others through these modalities to develop curiosity, question thoughts, live connected and empowered in what she's received as, "Living the Softer Way."**

**Raelin regularly shares the messages from WE are WE on her Facebook pages and show, *Raediance; Shine from Within,* and is the co-host of, *RE-turning to Clarity*, with her friend and fellow Healer, Laura Mazzotta; where they discuss navigating Spiritual-Awakening in today's hyper-driven climate to perform.**

**You can find replays of her shows and guided meditations on her YouTube Channels at:**

**https://www.youtube.com/channel/UCgLONcwaUkK5vg6HLPmn3Ng/**
**https://studio.youtube.com/channel/UCYjVpuAaNa_2TME5yXhlzmQ**

**Connect with Raelin at:**
**http://raelinsaindon.com**
**www.facebook.com/thehealingspaceco/**

**Join her FREE Group~ "Connected Empowerment" on FB at:**
**https://www.facebook.com/groups/255528564512039/**

CHAPTER 13

# Breathwork

## Breathe Your Way to Vitality

BY KAREN TASTO, CPC, E-RYT

### My Story

I spent the first 30 years of my life holding my breath. At an early age, I started to suck in my belly to appear slimmer, as culture modeled at the time. Consequently, I became a tense, anxious, and tired adult woman. Little did I know that the answer to revitalizing my energy was literally right under my nose. Breathwork saved me from continuing this way of being. Breathwork as a tool can be your path too to feeling calm, balanced, vibrant, and alive.

I was in yoga class when I first learned about breathwork. I was a new mom of two babies, one year apart. My weekly yoga class was the one reprieve I gave myself. I had dabbled in yoga while living in Boulder in my 20's where my teachers probably were providing breathing cues, but I wasn't ready to listen.

At the right time with the right teacher, I discovered I was what they called a "reverse breather." This meant I was sucking in my belly with each inhale and barely moving my body with my exhales. This is the opposite of how we want an optimal breath to move us. Observe any young child breathing, and you'll know what I mean by an optimal breath. Young children naturally breathe with their whole bodies. Ever wonder why kids have so much exuberance for life? It links back to their open and free breathing.

Because of my reversed breathing pattern, I particularly experienced confusion in yoga classes when asked to breathe in or out during a particular phase of the movement. I soon discovered that this confused breathing pattern was literally cutting off my life force energy.

At the time, I knew nothing about the anatomy or physiology of the breath. All I knew was that I felt tense, constricted, low on energy, and high on anxiety. Around this time, I happened upon Donna Farhi's book, *The Breathing Book*, where I learned that I probably picked up this pattern as a young teen from a culture that emphasized flat tummies. This message extends back in time as we see through the use of corsets, girdles, and just the plain old trick of sucking in the tummy. I can remember looking at myself sideways in a full-length mirror, hand on my tummy, and with a big inhale, sucking my soft belly in and up. I'd think to myself, *Could I walk around all day like this?* Well, soon enough, I was.

Also, breathing is contagious. This means we unconsciously emulate breathing patterns of others around us. When our parents or caregivers aren't breathing optimally, we begin to breathe in the same way. These patterns stay with us throughout adulthood unless we become aware enough to work on changing them. The good news is that a deeper breath is more contagious than a shallow breath. For example, if you're in an elevator where everyone is breathing shallowly but someone steps in and breathes deeply, the rest of the people in the elevator will unconsciously breathe more deeply than they were before. This knowledge meant I could now see how I picked up this breathing pattern. If I knew more about its source, I felt like I wasn't born breathing this way and could heal it. We came into this world knowing how to breathe, just as we came in being our true selves. These are so linked. As we come home to our natural optimal full breath, we come home to our full true selves. I was experiencing this firsthand.

Over time with solid practices like I'll share with you here, I developed my optimal breath pattern. I noticed my energy increasing and my demeanor becoming calmer.

When I began teaching yoga, I witnessed over and over, the

shallow breathing in others even when I, as a teacher, was persistently encouraging fuller breathing. I began to question with a bit of frustration in my desire to serve, why it was that people so resisted their own breath. So, I turned the question back on myself. *Why did I resist my own full breath?*

Of course, the more we teach something, the more we learn about ourselves. Not to mention, there is much learning in our resistance. What I ultimately learned was that my resistance to breathing fully related to my resistance to feeling, specifically to feeling my repressed emotions. We are not a culture that encourages much expression of grief or rage.

Later in my yoga teaching career, I came across the work of Max Strom, who emphasized open mouth breathing as compared to my past yoga training of only breathing through the nose. We tend to hold much tension in our jaw and mouth, which links to other areas of the body where we hold emotion. Open-mouthed breathing with yoga or as a stand-alone practice was revolutionary for me in helping me to free old emotions from my body while also keeping current emotions moving through me rather than getting stuck in me. After practice with him, old grief I had repressed from my sister's death nearly 20 years ago surfaced, and I found I could finally begin grieving her death.

At a point in my late 40's, I was feeling so small and constricted within myself from a lifetime of holding back and suppressing that it became more painful than the fear of breaking free and living big. I stepped onto a personal growth path where I eventually experienced the works of Regena Thomashauer and Layla Martin. This is where I experienced the practices of embodiment for not only emotional release but pleasure too. This meant taking what I knew from my years of breathwork and combining it with spontaneous movement and free expression of voice. This is what has taken my breathwork to a whole other realm, feeling for once, free, open, expressive, grounded in the body and anchored in my true self.

As a life coach, breathwork is the first tool I guide my clients through to help them access their bodies, their emotions, their energy centers, and their inner selves. Breath is also the portal to heightened self-awareness and intuition.

## The Tool

I'm providing you here a wide range of practices for breathwork that I use and that I've found to be easy and beneficial for my coaching clients. You can find a vast array of breathing practices through other resources, particularly yoga-based books. In yoga, the practice of breathwork is called "pranayama."

The biggest concept to understand in the practice of breathwork is actually that it not be work at all. The more we can get out of our own way, the better we can come home to our optimal breath.

More amazing aspects of breathwork:

- No special tools or props are needed.
- Breath is always available anytime, anywhere.
- Breathwork is free, easy, and powerful.
- Breathwork is contagious, so your practice affects all those around you.
- You could notice shifts in your energy just after a few minutes of practice.

Guidelines to keep in mind:

- Listen to your body and be gentle with yourself.
- Focus on breathing more in the belly and less in the chest.
- A complete exhale gives rise to a fuller inhale.
- Welcome whatever arises. Invite your emotions, resistances, fears, sensations to be your teacher.
- You might wish to journal after each breathing session with the journaling prompt, "What I noticed was..."
- Set up reminders throughout your day to take 5-minute breathing breaks.

- I highly recommend if you are new to breathwork that you spend plenty of time with the Healing Breath before pursuing the others. There are many other breath-holding patterns than the one I described here. Sticking with the Healing Breath practice will aid you in uncovering your optimal breath.
- If at any time through practices 2-6 you experience shortness of breath or dizziness, discontinue that practice for now and return back to the first practice, the Healing Breath.

## The Practices

Besides the written practices below, you can find my recordings of these same practices at https://karentasto.com/resources/

1. **Healing Breath** – This is best done lying down with the feet flat on the floor, knees bent. Place a hand softly on your lower belly, just below the navel. Without trying to change your breath in any way, simply notice the gentle rise and fall of your belly. If you don't feel any movement, keep your attention on your belly and your hand resting there. Notice any other movements or sensations as you allow your body to breathe you. Observe with curiosity. After a few minutes of observation with hand on belly, place your hands on your lower side ribs with elbows and shoulders relaxed. With every exhale draw the navel down towards the spine. With every inhale expand the side ribs out like an accordion, while keeping the belly soft and relaxed. Exhale, pulling navel down towards the spine. Continue this way, maintaining a relaxed state throughout. Your body knows how to optimally breath so don't force. Breathe at a comfortable pace. Just let the body show you. Surrender to the breath. Stay with this for at least 5 minutes and up to 20 minutes.

2. **Releasing Breath** – This is best done standing with the feet planted firmly on the ground. First, exhale fully. Now inhale deeply through the nose from the depth of your belly, expanding the

abdomen and rib cage out to the sides like an accordion. Exhale with the mouth wide open and make the sound, "Hah," until you've reached the end of the exhale, with the navel pulled back towards the spine. Allow the jaw, the throat, and the shoulders to relax throughout. Practice this breath for at least 5-10 minutes. Observe any emotions rising to the surface and welcome them like you would an old friend.

3. **Calming Breath** – This is best done sitting or lying down. Use the same breathing instructions from the Releasing Breath described above but with counting. Exhale completely. Inhale for a count of 4 seconds. Exhale then for a count of 8 seconds. The idea is to breathe at a ratio of 2:1. Exhale for twice the count as you inhale. If it only feels good to inhale for 3 seconds, then exhale for 6. Practice this breath anytime you're feeling stressed or anxious. It's also a perfect practice at bedtime or before a big event or talk. Just a few minutes will leave you feeling soothed and relaxed.

4. **Resetting Breath** – The Calming Breath above should feel really comfortable before you attempt this practice. This is best done sitting up tall or standing. To begin, exhale completely with the sound of "hah." Inhale with mouth open to the count of 4. Now pause at the top of your inhale for a count of 7. Exhale with mouth open for a count of 8, making the sound "hah." Continue this pattern. This is also called the 4-7-8 breath. If any phase of this practice feels straining, simply speed up the counting. Just keep the 4-7-8 ratio for all three phases. After a few minutes of this practice, it feels like a reset for your entire being. It helps regulate the hormone cortisol, which controls your fight or flight response.

5. **Balancing Breath** – This is best done sitting or lying down. This practice is about breathing in and out of each chakra center, bringing healthy functioning and harmony to your entire being. With your attention on your pelvic floor, breathe in and out of this area for four long, deep breaths. Notice any movement here. Then

move your attention up to your lower belly below the navel and take four deep breaths in and out of this chakra. Next, bring your attention to your solar plexus, taking four deep breaths in your power chakra. Move your focus to your heart and breathe fully in and out of the heart space for four breaths. Then move to your throat for four breaths. Next, bring your attention to your third eye for four long breaths. Lastly, go to the top of your head, your crown chakra. Breathe in and out of your head. Finish with one last integrating breath, inhaling up the back body, and exhaling down the front body.

**6. Pleasure Breath** – This is best done sitting cross-legged on the edge of a cushion or folded blanket with your hands on your thighs. Use the same breath as instructed in the Releasing Breath practice while adding visualization and movement. Start by visualizing a radiant ball of energy that holds all kinds of goodness resting at the center of your pelvis. Make some hip circles, mixing up this good energy. Feel the ball expand. Take four breaths in and out of the pelvis. Now with every inhale, bring the ball from the pelvis up to the lower belly, rocking forward. With every exhale, drop it down to the pelvis with the sound of "hah," rocking back on your tailbone. Repeat for four breaths. Now with your inhale, bring the ball up behind the navel, with your exhale push the ball back down to the pelvis again for four breaths while rocking back and forth. Don't forget to make the sound of "hah." Next, on inhales, pull the ball up to behind the heart. On exhales, drop it back down to the pelvis, again rocking for four breaths. Then pull the ball up to the back of the throat with inhales, rocking forward. Drop the ball down to the pelvis with exhales, rocking back. Repeat for four breaths. Now, picture the ball moving up on inhales to the back of your head and dropping down to pelvis with exhales. Lastly, bring the ball up to the crown of the head with inhales, and dropping it down to the pelvis on exhales. Finish by breathing once again in and out of the pelvis for four breaths, feeling your entire body tingling or humming. Rest your hands about 2 inches below your navel, your center of gravity, and collect all that tingling sensation from the body into this center. Enjoy!

---

**Karen Tasto, CPC, E-RYT200, is the owner of Open Heart Healing. She helps women tune in and turn on to their feminine powers so they can live in their fullest, most free expression of themselves. Her 15 years as a yoga teacher, guiding her students back home to their breath & vitality, were the foundation for her work now as a certified women's empowerment life coach, Sacred Circle facilitator, and Reiki Master. She also leads workshops and life-changing retreats.**

**Karen is passionate about helping women break out of their good-girl ways so they can awaken all aspects of themselves and reclaim their wholeness. She most loves to gather women together in circle where they feel safe and supported to show up as their real selves and go deep. She knows from her own experiences that the way to a woman's freedom is through her body, her emotions, and sisterhood.**

**Karen's a recovering good girl, a longtime seeker, a tree hugger, dancer, mom of three young adult boys, and resides in the DC Metro area. Married to her soulmate and college sweetheart, this intimate relationship is her greatest barometer of personal growth. Learn more about her at https://KarenTasto.com and https://karentasto.com/resources/.**

CHAPTER 14

# Acupressure

## The Points are the Key to Feeling Better

BY NIKKI RICHMAN, M.AC, L.AC

Life isn't linear, and thank goodness for that! My name is Nikki Richman, and I have been an acupuncturist for seven years, and I absolutely love what I do. I couldn't have found a more perfect career for me, and yet I totally fell into acupuncture by accident.

Most people, when they decide to train as an acupuncturist, have been having regular acupuncture, have directly seen the amazing results or transformations that happen in their lives, and think, *that's what I want to do with my life.* When I decided to train as an acupuncturist, I'd never even had acupuncture! I knew it involved needles and came from China, but that was the extent of my knowledge. So how did I get into acupuncture?

I find people fascinating, I have a psychology background, and I'd spent over 10 years working with adults and adolescents with mental health issues. I took some time off work to be a stay-at-home mom, and when my kids were toddlers, I started to look at courses I could do. Every year I would find something that looked interesting, family therapy, group psychotherapy. I'd excitedly announce to the world, "I'm going to train to be a family therapist," or "I'm going to train to be a psychotherapist." Then for whatever reason,

I would procrastinate and not apply for these courses. Finally, one year I decided I needed to find something to do, and I was embarrassed about never following through after telling people I was going to do a specific training. So I decided this would be the year (2005) when I would find a course and actually get on it.

Growing up I'd had a very unconventional mother, who really was ahead of her time. We would go to alternative health fairs in the 1970's and we'd go and visit color therapists and spiritual healers. This led me to always having an interest in health and wellness, so I started to look at courses on nutrition and homeopathy. My best friend in England is an Acupuncturist, and I was discussing the different courses I was exploring with her. She said, "Nikki, why don't you look into training to be an acupuncturist, I think it would be perfect for you." At that point, I'd never ever considered training to be an acupuncturist. Still, as soon as I started looking at what acupuncture involved, I knew that acupuncture was what I was meant to be studying.

Right from the beginning of my studies, I loved how Acupuncture and Chinese Medicine viewed the body and health and wellness. It's very poetic and beautiful and profound. What I love about acupuncture is that it is such a complete system of medicine, it treats the body on a physical, emotional, and spiritual level.

## The Tool

### HOW DOES ACUPUNCTURE WORK?

Acupuncture teaches there are channels or meridians running up and down the body which belong to specific organs of the body. For example, lung meridian, or stomach meridian. On these channels, at specific parts of the body, face, and head are acupuncture points, which, when stimulated either by an acupuncture needle or acupressure, have a certain influence on the body. For example, acupuncture points can help digestion, headaches, toothache, back pain, anxiety, or insomnia, to name a few. The acupuncture points help bring the body back into balance, to a state of homeostasis.

Stimulating the points will bring circulation to a specific area and help to decrease inflammation.

One of the things I like to do for my acupuncture patients is to provide tools and strategies so that they have means of treating specific physical or emotional conditions themselves at home. I do this by teaching specific acupuncture points on their body that they can massage and stimulate.

In this chapter, I'm going to teach you a few of my favorite acupuncture points that you can apply acupressure to or massage in order to treat different conditions. I particularly like points that have several functions, giving you more bang for your buck!

On my website www.metsuyanwellness.com, I have a resource page, and you will be able to see a picture of each of the points I'm going to teach you.

## How to do acupressure

There is no right or wrong way to do acupressure. Do what feels comfortable for you. You can use your finger or thumb, or you can use a pen or chopstick to stimulate the point. You can either massage the point with a circular motion or you can press on the acupuncture point. Try different levels of pressure and see what feels good for you. I would advise stimulating an acupressure point for between one to three minutes.

## The points

Pericardium 6 – (Nei Guan) – Inner Gate

Location – Pericardium 6 (PC-6) is located on the palm side of the wrist, a couple of inches up the arm between the two tendons. If you place 3 fingers on your wrist crease, starting with your ring finger, where your index finger rests is where PC-6 is located.

Nausea – PC-6 is the go-to point to treat nausea, whether it's nausea from morning sickness, motion sickness, or chemotherapy. I use this point a lot with my pregnant patients and patients undergoing chemotherapy to help their nausea. You can buy bands from the pharmacy called "Sea Bands" for travel sickness or nausea, they are wrist bands with a magnet or ball sewn in them that stimulate PC-6.

Anxiety – PC-6 is also a great point for treating anxiety. One of PC-6 main functions is that it unbinds the chest. So if you are feeling stressed and anxious and one of the symptoms you experience is that your chest feels tight, you get heart palpitations, or you feel like you can't take a deep breath, massaging PC-6 while taking a few slow deep breaths can be very helpful for calming your anxiety.

Insomnia – PC-6 has a calming effect on anxiety, it's also a beneficial point to use for insomnia. If you're lying in bed and can't sleep because you have things on your mind, this is a really useful point to be massaging to calm yourself and help you fall back to sleep.

Relationship break-up / heartbreak – PC-6's name is Inner Gate. In Western Medicine, the pericardium is the membrane that surrounds the heart. In Chinese Medicine from an emotional point of view, Inner Gate can be opened or closed depending upon what experiences we want our heart to have. Sometimes when we have been hurt by a relationship ending our tendency can be to shut the gate around our heart and not let anyone in, massaging this point can allow you to connect with others in a way that feels safe.

Stomach 36 – (Zu San Li) – Leg Three Miles

Location – Stomach 36 (ST-36) is on the outside of the shin. If you place 4 fingers on the bottom of your kneecap, starting with your index finger, with your fingers facing outwards, ST-36 is where your little finger lies. From the level of your little finger, if you move slightly laterally (outwards), your finger will fall into a dip, which is ST-36.

Digestion – because ST-36 is on the stomach meridian, this is a great point to regulate your digestion. If you don't have an appetite, this can stimulate your appetite. This can help balance blood sugars and reduce cravings. It helps treat diarrhea, constipation, stomach bloating, stomach-ache, hiccups, and indigestion.

Immune Boosting – ST-36 is my go-to point for boosting people's immune systems. I call it my "Chicken Soup" point. It's a great point for people who have had a chronic illness or an auto-immune condition, this is one point that I would recommend massaging every day.

Fatigue – ST-36 is great for giving you energy when you're tired. Its name is Leg Three Miles, in the olden days when soldiers in the Chinese Army were exhausted from marching for hours, this point would be stimulated, and they could walk for another three miles, hence the name Leg Three Miles! If you're a runner, this is an excellent point to massage.

Breast Pain / Mastitis – the stomach meridian goes up the front of the body, and through the breasts, massaging ST-36 can be very helpful for a new mom with mastitis.

Liver 3 – (Tai Chong) – Great Rushing

Location – Liver 3 (LR-3) is on the top of the foot, between the big toe and second toe. From the webbing between these two toes, if you gently rub your finger along the top of your foot, you fall into a big dip/depression – this is LR-3.

Getting things flowing/moving – This is a brilliant point for when you're feeling stuck, be it physically or emotionally. If you're feeling frustrated, stressed, feel like you're going to explode at someone, this is a great point to massage, it helps the emotions flow, it's a great point for someone having PMS. On a physical level, if your muscles are feeling tight, achy, or you're getting muscle cramps/

spasms, this is a great point to massage, as it sends blood to the muscles.

Eye Issues – LR-3 is great for treating a variety of eye issues, redness, dryness, itchy, allergies.

Issues affecting your head – LR-3 is a great point to use if you have a headache or are feeling dizzy. Or when you feel really angry about something, and you feel the energy rush to your head. Think about those cartoons with steam coming out of the person's ears!! LR-3 is a great point to calm everything down and stop things rushing up to your head.

Large Intestine 4 – (He Gu) – Joining Valley

Location – The location of LR-3 on the foot matches the location of Large Intestine 4 (LI-4) on the hand. LI-4 is on the back of the hand between your thumb and index finger. If you go from the webbing, you fall into a dip in the belly of the muscle, it often feels a bit tender. WARNING – do not massage this point if you are pregnant, as it may induce labor.

Issues of the face – LI-4 is a great point for issues of the face if you're experiencing a headache, toothache, jaw pain, TMJ, nosebleed, sinus issues, or nasal congestion. LI-4 is a really easy point to massage, so very helpful if you have a headache or toothache.

Cold / Flu symptoms – LI-4 is a great point to massage if you have a cold or flu and are experiencing symptoms such as chills, fever, runny nose, sore throat, scratchy throat, sweating issue, body aches. Massaging LI-4 can help the symptoms pass more quickly.

Large Intestine 20 – (Ying Xiang) – Welcome Fragrance

Location – If you go the bottom of your nostrils and move your fingers out to the nasolabial groove, the lines that come down from your nose, that's Large Intestine 20 (LI-20).

Opens the nose – I have lots of patients with allergies, sinus issues, nasal congestion, and this is my go-to point to relieve them of their congestion and help them breathe again. I joke that this point is my party trick point because it works so quickly. If someone is skeptical about whether acupuncture works, I needle this point, and people are amazed at how quickly their congestion clears. I particularly love the name of this point. Welcome Fragrance. I had a new patient who had lost her sense of smell for a few months, and after doing some other acupuncture points plus LI-20, her sense of smell started to return the following day!

Kidney 1 – (Yong Quan) – Bubbling Spring

Location – Kidney 1 (KI-1) is on the sole of the foot, between the 2nd and 3rd toe, just behind the ball of the foot (1/3 from the base of the 2nd toe, 2/3 from the back of the heel).

Grounding / Calming – KI-1 is the only acupuncture point on the sole of the foot. I love this point because it connects us to the earth. I often tell my patients to be barefooted and stand outside on the grass and gently stamp their feet to stimulate this point. This is a good point for helping to lower blood pressure.

Insomnia – This is a great point for people who are in their heads all the time and find it hard to switch their thoughts off, it descends things from the head. I often recommend this point to people with insomnia. You can be sitting up in bed, and massage this point, it's also a good point to rub some lavender oil on. This is also a great point to massage on children before they go to sleep. If your children have that burst of energy before they go to sleep and you just need them to settle and get ready for bed, this is a great point to be part of your bedtime routine.

Getting Going – KI-1 is a great point to massage when you want to do something, but fear is holding you back. It gives you that oomph to start something new despite the apprehension.

---

**Originally from England, Nikki Richman is passionate about health & wellbeing and helping people feel their best. Before training as an acupuncturist, Nikki worked in the field of psychology with adults and adolescents with mental health and emotional issues for over 10 years. Observing how a person's emotional health affected their physical health and how a person's physical health affected their well-being, she wanted to retrain in a modality that could address both issues. Nikki began her Acupuncture training in England and studied there for three years, before moving to the US and training for a further three years.**

**Nikki's acupuncture practice Metsuyan Wellness is located in North Bethesda, MD. Metsuyan is the Hebrew word for "Excellent," and Nikki wants her patients to have excellent wellness. You can find out more about how acupuncture can help you at www.metsuyanwellness.com and see health and wellness tips that Nikki shares on https://www.facebook.com/MetsuyanWellness/**

CHAPTER 15

# Trigger Point Release

## Resolving Muscular Pain

BY DR. STACY SNOW, PT, DPT

## My Story

I paused for a moment and closed my eyes before slipping my finger under the flap to open the manila envelope that had just arrived in the mail.

I pulled the papers out without opening my eyes and took a deep breath. Did I make it? Did I actually get in? Surely it must be good news if this is a big manilla envelope and not just a skinny white one, right?

It took a few minutes with my heart beating out of my chest before I was able to open my eyes and look at the contents of that precious brown manilla envelope.

I breathed out an involuntary sigh of relief as I read the words, 'Congratulations! We are excited to inform you of your acceptance to the Doctor of Physical Therapy program...'

I sat down with my head in my hands, still holding on to those papers and cried tears of joy and relief. I had worked so hard over the past 3 years for this moment. Sacrificed time with family and friends. Said no to invites so I could stay home and study. I took the prerequisite classes I hadn't had in undergrad, including retaking Chemistry twice, my nemesis, and the only class that had ever made me feel like I might have a learning disability.

I spent countless hours in the library after work studying for the GRE, trying to get myself to memorize vocabulary I'd never heard of and knew I'd never actually use in real life. I kept pushing forward because I always knew I wanted to be a physical therapist. Ever since high school, when I learned there was a career that could combine my love of health and athletics, allow me to help people in ways that really mattered, and not be stuck behind a desk all day, I knew that I was hooked.

When I got that letter in the mail that day and realized that I was one of the 40 other people getting that same brown manilla envelope out of the more than 400 applicants, something in me shifted. I knew my life's purpose was starting to emerge. I knew I had done the hard work I needed to do to allow it to emerge. I had shown up, and now I was starting to see the rewards of all that effort and sacrifice.

I was so excited to see the path that was starting to lay out before me. My husband and I had just bought a condo across the street from the school I'd be going to. I'd be able to walk to class and spend every free second studying without having to worry about the commute. We were in a good place, and I knew after my program was finished, we'd be ready to start a family. I'd always wanted to have a meaningful career that I loved, and I'd always wanted to be a mom. Everything was coming together, and it was even better than I'd imagined!

Except...the Universe had another plan in mind, and that's not how it happened.

At least not at first.

In November of that year, three months into the Doctorate program that I had worked so tirelessly to get into, my adoring husband, the one who I knew I was going to marry on the very first day we met, came home from a work trip abroad and told me he didn't want to be married anymore, and just like that, the bottom fell out of my life.

*Sometimes the Universe has different plans than what we have in mind.*

Sometimes the Universe can see things we can't, or never want to see. Sometimes the Universe knows what's best for us and sends out an SOS to save us when it knows we would never save ourselves.

My husband leaving so suddenly, and in the heart-shattering way he did it, threw me to my knees in a way I had never known was possible. I was suddenly tossed into a place of insecurity, of betrayal, of so many lies that I didn't know the truth anymore. I was hurt, enraged, scared, sad, broken, *and* I was in the third month of the doctorate program that I had spent the past 3 years of my life sacrificing time with friends, studying for hours on end, trying to make a better life for myself to get into.

I suddenly found myself at the lowest point of my life in the midst of a program that would require every ounce of my mind, body, and soul to be at the top of their game in order to not fail. I didn't know how I could possibly succeed.

I realized I had to decide.

Was I going to give up, to crawl into my bed, pull the covers up over my ears, and stay there until the pain went away and give up on my degree because I was too broken to show up for class every day? Or was I going to pick myself up from the bottom of the pile of muck that was thrown on top of me, dust myself off, and kick myself in the butt to get back into that seat in a class that I had earned?

I chose the latter.

I chose to show up.

I chose me.

I realized that right then and there I had to choose if I was going to win, or if I was going to let myself lose, despite the circumstances that were out of my control. I knew I had to do it for me, and somewhere deep inside, I knew I had to do it for someone else too. I didn't know at the time who that *someone* else was, but I knew there were people out there who needed me to brush myself off and get back to work because they needed my help. I knew I had a mission that was bigger than me, bigger than my heartache, and even though I needed every ounce of my energy just to breathe, never mind get out of bed and do anything productive, I had to do it. I had a bigger purpose in life, and the Universe stepped in to take my hand on the new detour that was suddenly blasted out in front of me.

My divorce dragged on for three long years, the entire length of grad school, and it required me to dig deep to find the resources that would help me succeed and not personally crumble. Chronic and constant stress and adrenaline became my new norm. Anger, pain, and cortisol coursed through my veins. My vision of having fun and making lifelong friends in grad school instead became learning how to just keep it together and survive.

I was glad to have the distraction of school to keep me going, but times were tough. During one anatomy lab exam while I was silently walking around a line of bodies with my entire class, I had to keep wiping away my persistently falling tears while attempting to identify body parts in the cadavers while my classmates pretended not to notice. I had to hide my tears sitting in nearly every class and in group study sessions for the first two years of the program. I had to learn how to study while my mind was incessantly playing the life-altering conversations with my husband on a loop over and over so I could continue with my work because getting 3 B-'s over the course of the program meant I would fail.

It was on that hard road that I discovered the tools that have become part of my holistic physical therapy practice. The tools that helped me to not give up, to keep pushing forward, to do what I had to do, to stand up for myself, and be the rock that I needed to be. I look back sometimes and am amazed that I was able to get through that time in one piece. That I didn't just crumble into dust and blow away in the wind. But the hard times we go through often carry our greatest gifts. I learned that I was stronger than I knew, that I was more resilient than I believed, that I would bend and not break under pressure. I learned to trust my instincts, to believe in myself, to have faith that I had the tools within me to succeed. I learned that the only way out is through, that you can't bury your feelings, you have to bravely face them if you want them to lose their power over you.

I learned that grief is a process and a tool and that it can help you get to know yourself on a deeper level than you ever imagined possible if you let it do its work and don't try to shove it down and hide it.

Divorce is one of the most stressful things that a human being can experience. It's like a death, and it does its best to drag you down to the bottom kicking and screaming until you finally stop to look around you and realize there's nowhere else to go but up.

Successfully navigating through a divorce or any life-altering event can make you realize that you are strong and resilient, and when it comes down to it, you can handle anything that comes your way. While I would never want to learn that lesson twice, I can recognize and appreciate that I went through that experience for a reason. I now measure every other challenge that comes up in my life against that barometer, and it helps me to realize that if I could get through that, I can get through anything.

My entire philosophy for how I practice as a holistic practitioner is centered around that experience, and I've come to believe it to be one of my life's most meaningful gifts. I use the tools in my practice that I learned out of necessity; the things that helped me to survive and step up to do what I needed to do to get through the hardest emotional challenge of my life while simultaneously learning how not to fail in the hardest intellectual endeavor of my life.

That experience forced me to learn some of my most valuable life lessons, wisdom I've now passed on to my clients. I learned the importance of letting yourself be vulnerable, the benefits of leaning on the people who love you when you need it, the wisdom of listening to your intuition, the vital skill of taking care of your body and mindset, and the importance of eating nutritious food to nourish your cells. I learned that yoga could be a religion, that meditation quiets the chatter in your brain, that asking 'God, Grandma, and the Universe' for help really does bring answers.

Through this death and life experience, I also learned that the mission of my work extends beyond just helping clients feel better physically. I help them improve all areas of their life by focusing on their health and self-care and ultimately living up to a greater vision than they can initially see for themselves. I give them the tools to live their healthiest and best life so they can have the strength and confidence to live up to their true potential and create their own positive ripple effect in the world. I teach that your circumstances don't have to become your reality, you have the power to choose how you respond to what shows up in your life.

The lessons and tools that I learned through those hard months and years became the foundation for who I am as a practitioner. They helped me to see what people really need to feel healthy, strong, and fulfilled and to live a life of meaning and purpose. My goal coming out on the other side is to help my clients dig deep into what's really important to them and to have the resources and support to make it a reality. I have many tools in my toolbox to help make this happen, and the one I will share with you here is one that will help give you your power back over your body. To help you help yourself without having to depend on anyone else to do it. To release the stress that your body has accumulated as it's telling you it needs your attention. To independently release the muscular pain that shows up to speak to you when your self-care has gotten off track.

So if you're ready to start taking control of how you feel, to have the tools to treat yourself, to release the tension that has built up over a lifetime so you can show up as healthy and happy as possible, read on!

## The Tool

**What you'll need:** A tennis or lacrosse ball and a wall.

**What to keep in mind:** The sensations you feel should be described as a 'good hurt.' It should never be painful and something that feels like it's the 'wrong' thing to do.

**Exercise:** You can find a short video demonstrating this Trigger Point Release Technique at: https://tranquilplacept.com/self-care-resources

Find a place where you won't be interrupted with a wall with blank space that you can lean against. Take the tennis or lacrosse ball and put it behind your back and gently lean your body against it so it's holding in a spot against the wall.

**Note:** There are a couple of differences in the tennis ball and the lacrosse ball. The tennis ball is softer and has more 'give' so the sensation will be less intense when you do this exercise. It will also be more likely to slip out from behind you due to its fuzzy outer coating so if you prefer this style of ball but find it doesn't stay in place, then you can try slipping the ball into a pillowcase and holding the end of the pillowcase as you do the exercise. This way, the ball will stay in place, and you won't be spending your time chasing it around the room!

The lacrosse ball is a more dense material, so the sensation will be more intense. It will provide a deeper massage, and only light pressure is required. It also has more of a 'sticky' outer coating, so it's less likely to fly out from behind you during your treatment! Choose the type of ball that gives you that 'good hurt' sensation, and it feels like a comfortable deep massage. Once you have the ball in place behind your shoulder or in between your shoulder blade and spine, you'll want to apply light pressure and then gently move your body up and down, so the ball is rolling on the muscles beside your spine. Focus on slow and deep breathing as you do this, moving up and down for 1-2 minutes. Pay attention to areas that feel especially tight, and after a minute or two of rolling, find one of the tender points with the ball and hold light pressure on that particular spot. This spot is called a trigger point, which is a band of taut muscles that have gotten 'stuck' in a shortened position. Trigger points indicate a source of stress in the body and can cause pain and tension in other seemingly unrelated areas. By releasing them, you'll free up your muscles and joints to move more effectively the way they're meant to.

As you're holding light pressure on the tender spot, close your eyes, and focus on taking deep breaths until you can feel the sensation lessening, and you feel the spot 'release.' This will usually take around 90 seconds, but some trigger points may take more or less time. Once you feel the initial spot release and the discomfort lessen, find another tight and tender spot and repeat the process. As you do this, try to relax your body and drop your shoulders down and away from your ears. Try to notice any areas that are holding tension and consciously relax them as you release the trigger points in your shoulder and back.

Once you have released all of the trigger points that you can find, remove the ball from the wall, and gently move your body in whatever ways it tells you it needs. Try stretching your arms overhead, back behind you, and grasp your hands behind your back and reach up. Roll your neck to the left shoulder, down, and to the right shoulder in a semi-circle, and repeat to the other side. See how the muscles and movement feel after releasing the trigger points that were restricting them. Take a deep breath, smile, and enjoy the release!

---

**Dr. Stacy Snow, PT, DPT is a Doctor of Physical Therapy, a human movement specialist, and a holistic physical therapist. She is a lifelong advocate of self-development and helps her clients create a plan to optimize their health and self-care in order to release their full potential in every other area of their life.**

**Stacy is the founder of Tranquil Place Physical Therapy & Wellness, a private practice in Northern Virginia, and the creator of the Purposeful Body Method. She uses a combination of movement science, hands-on manual therapy treatments, mindset training, lifestyle coaching, whole food nutrition guidance, and self-care habits to help empower her clients with the physical and mental strength, inspiration, and confidence they need to live their best life.**

Stacy's the mom of a future world-changing little girl, a functional performance coach helping her clients reach peak performance and an advocate for helping people become the best version of themselves. When she's not at work helping people to move better, feel better, and perform better, you can find her at home with her husband, daughter, and Australian cattle dog/lab mix Cody, or at the boxing gym or yoga studio.

To see if Dr. Stacy's method would help you excel to optimal levels in your own life, you can find out more about her programs at www.tranquilplacept.com.

## CHAPTER 16

# Self-Spinal Mobilization

## Mobilization for Pain Relief & Strong Posture

### BY ERIKA L. PUTNAM, DC, RYT-500

It takes guts to be a chiropractor. I have been called rogue, renegade, wild child, and the very distasteful, bone cracker. When I decided to become a chiropractic physician, I knew I was swimming upstream. My mother worked in a hospital as a social worker. She was surrounded by "real" doctors and questioned my career path and rejected the profession's credibility. She did not approve, initially. I committed to the profession anyway.

As a young girl, I witnessed my father take on the sport of running. He would run before daybreak and return to lift weights while I got ready for school. Fitness was present in the background of our house, and it included my awareness of his daily exercise routine, happy attitude, and positive body image. He played college football and knew about exercise, but with marriage, a career, and beer, he morphed into an overweight American man. That changed one day in his mid-thirties when he saw a picture of himself in swim trunks on the beach in Mexico. In his words, "That big ole' beer belly has got to go." Then and there, he set out to be a runner.

I wanted to be a runner too, and on occasion, he would take me with him. I would try to run a mile with him, but usually, I ended up holding on to the back of his shorts while he pulled me the last quarter of a mile home. I never fell in love with running, but because I stayed in shape, we did active things together.

My fitness came from participating in high school basketball, volleyball, and the dance team. However, my passion was the sport of rodeo. When my parents got divorced, I tasted freedom. At the age of fourteen, I started driving and hauling my horse to local arenas to practice and to compete in rodeos across the state. Horseback riding takes flexibility, strength, and balance. I took it for granted. I was young, and fitness was the natural byproduct of my hobby.

Fitness wove into adventures with my father. I rode horses in the backcountry with my dad. Perhaps this is where my attitude about perseverance began. With horses and weather and tough country, there were usually problems. What might be rebellious to some was my way of taking a stand for things I believed in. I learned to be brave with my dad on hunting trips. He left me alone for hours while he scouted for deer. I stayed behind watching for game and managing the pack string. I wasn't in danger, but it was a big task for a young girl. He had a standing rule to always get back on your horse. It was as much a lesson for me, as the horse. He believed you should stay with challenges, figure them out, and go again until things worked out how you wanted them to. In his own way, he taught me to address the cause of problems. He showed me prevention could be the best solution if we took the time to take a more in-depth look at things and situations.

We hunted caribou together in remote Alaskan bear country. We hiked with heavy packs, slept in a soft-sided tent, and our only communication was to wave a flag if a pilot happened to fly by during the ten-day trip. My dad wasn't trying to make me tough. He was sharing the kind of experiences and adventures he appreciated. Our trips taught me to believe in myself and to be resourceful and prepared.

Dad was not only a teacher but an avid learner. We listened to country music and self-help cassettes when we traveled. I adopted his love of learning and self-inquiry. I took my first certification course at eighteen and started teaching aerobics. Teaching aerobics led me to manage a health club during college. I developed health as a mindset. I studied who succeeded and who dropped out. I had many majors. None ever quite felt right. Eventually, I settled on pre-physical therapy and dietetics. I knew I wanted to work in the health industry, but I had reservations about working with sick people, and I didn't like hospitals.

I wanted to be my own boss. No surprise. I didn't consider chiropractic as an option until I met several chiropractors who must have seen my strong and caring spirit and nudged me in their professional direction.

In 1989, my dad and his running buddy, John, a chiropractor, and I were out in the Idaho desert scouting for sheep. After a long hot day in the sagebrush, we were headed home. John and I were talking about my future and how I was recently accepted to the University of Kentucky dietetics program.

He said, "Erika, you are going to hate that."

My heart sank. I had been jumping through hoops to get accepted, and I was excited about college in famous horse country.

He continued, "I know you, and I don't think you are going to like feeding applesauce to sick people in the hospital all day. I think you should consider chiropractic."

I had to let his words sink in. "John," I said, "I am not smart enough to be a doctor."

He was sitting in the front seat of my dad's Jeep Cherokee. I will never forget the way he turned around to look at me and said, "What? Are you kidding me? Yes, you are! You are plenty smart enough, and you will help a lot of people."

It never occurred to me that I could be a doctor. I was a woman. Women weren't doctors. In high school, my counselors directed me into home economics, not math and science. It felt great to have someone believe in me, see my strengths, and reflect them back to me. *I could be a doctor.* Something I had not considered and even doubted. Whatever John saw in me and said to me, changed my life.

Within weeks I was working in a female chiropractor's office and watching people heal and get their lives and health back. I began to understand the philosophy of chiropractic as a natural holistic healthcare profession. I began to see an approach to the whole patient where the treatment was directed at correcting the cause and not just treating symptoms. The holistic philosophy appealed to me.

It's not easy being in a profession that's misunderstood. But being misunderstood does not mean ineffective. Chiropractic is powerful medicine. It aligns with my beliefs about wellness, prevention, personal responsibility, and a little bit of going against the grain. Say no to drugs, go for a run, lose weight, fix the problem, be proactive. Be on the same team as your body, care for, and respect it. Maybe even stand up to the popular belief that modern medicine has more power than our innate ability to heal.

Self-care is imperative. The more we do to prevent illness, injury, and preventable diseases, the better off we are. My interest in exercise and self-care is what led me to get certified in yoga eight years ago. After seventeen years in practice, I wanted to give patients more than exercises. I still wanted their spines aligned and their nervous systems functioning, but I also wanted them to have alignment in their minds, hearts, and spirits. Their stress was undoing the work we were doing together. And my stress was destroying my personal effectiveness as a physician.

When I found yoga, I began my own healing journey. I found a steadier mind, which resulted in a more balanced physical body. The benefits were strength and flexibility, but they were not the purpose of my yoga practice.

My initial attraction to yoga was the relief I experienced as I allowed emotions and tears that needed to be released flow onto the mat. I regained my personal and professional purpose through yoga, and I became even more intent on sharing a way for my patients to get well and stay well.

Back cracking, spinal manipulation, works. It's a thing of the past to not believe in it. It's the primary skill I offer in my clinic, and it takes guts to come from the heart. I am a "real" doctor. What I want people to know is that chiropractic works tenfold with clients who also have active self-care practices. What patients eat, do, and think can add to or take away from results. People are physical, chemical, and emotional, and we are only as strong as we proactively keep those systems.

After working on thousands of people, their bodies taught me. I began to see and embrace the concept of the body as a self-healing organized system made up of many biological systems working together. The parts make up the whole. What happens to one affects the whole. Damage to one part damages the whole, and caring for one part heals the whole. It became clear that we must actively support our health and actively remove interference to stay healthy and heal.

The belief and expectation in the potential of the body is the first step towards getting good results and outcomes. Treatment is as much the patient's responsibility as the doctor's. Even with good care, health is ultimately the result of our beliefs and behaviors. Examine them, know them, and change them if need be. In other words, get adjusted, on all levels of your being.

## The Tools:

I give my patients and yoga students similar spinal mobilization and postural techniques to strengthen and stretch the spine. The spine moves in 6 directions, and it's important to move all three spinal curves through each of those directions.

### THE GOALS ARE:

1. To undo what we do (hunch, sit too much, keep our heads forward, and our lower backs slouched).
2. To do what we don't do (reach overhead, lie flat on our backs, lift with our core, look side to side).

3. To have mindful awareness of full ranges of motion and move from and return to a strong and stable postural neutral.

## MOBILIZATION ACTIVITIES:

1. Spinal roll. This is good to mobilize the vertebra and ribs in the middle back or thoracic spine. It's fun and feels great. Lie flat on your back and then tuck yourself into a little ball. Gently, not violently, roll back and forth from head to buttocks or side to side. Keep a slight tuck in the chin to protect your neck. 3-5 times is usually enough to loosen things up.

2. Overhead reach. Stand with feet hip-distance apart with a very slight bend in your knees. Tilt your pelvis backward just a little bit as if you were making a "zip up your pants" gesture. Not too much, just enough to make sure your pelvis is in neutral. Not too arched and not too tucked. From here, inhale and reach your arms over your head, keep them about shoulder-distance apart. Reach your hands upward and try to straighten your elbows, look up to the sky, lengthening your neck, but don't drop your head backward, then lift from your chest or heart region upward and lengthen the mid-back region. Notice if this shifts your lower back or pelvis. If so, see if you can re-adjust back to that neutral spine, which may make you draw your navel to your spine and use your core more. From here, exhale and lower your arms. With that exhale, imagine you are pushing through water, and your midsection and spine are rising up as the arms go down. This exercise helps lengthen the latissimus dorsi muscle that goes from the lower back to the upper arms. This is also good for the thoracic spine, neck muscles, breathing muscles, and rib mobility. Sitting postures with the head forward or flexed shortens these muscles causing neck pain and breathing problems. Reaching overhead lengthens and strengthens many muscles. Do this 10 times per waking hour.

For a full version, one-hour yoga video of these tips and more, see the following website. https://thebendatwhitefish.com/resources/

---

**Dr. Erika Putnam, chiropractic physician, is the owner of The Bend in Whitefish, Montana. She uses a broad and holistic approach to treat spinal and extremity conditions and other health problems with a variety of chiropractic techniques, rehabilitation, nutrition, lifestyle, and functional medicine. She has over 20 years of experience in the chiropractic field and holds a 500-hour yoga instructor certification. The Bend has a private yoga studio where Dr. Putnam helps the public and chiropractic patients recover by engaging them in yoga or exercise instruction to prevent injuries from reoccurring and to improve overall strength and flexibility. She teaches anatomy education for yoga school teacher training programs. She advocates for healing in a pro-active environment that includes physical, emotional, and energetic wellbeing. Erika is an outdoors enthusiast who balances her work life by road bike cycling, hunting big game and seeking adventure and sanctity in mountains and rivers. In her spare time, she writes and dreams of owning her own dahlia farm.**

**For more information visit her at http://thebendatwhitefish.com or connect with her at 406-888-6044.**

CHAPTER 17

# Myofascial Release

## The Wisdom of the Fascia

BY IZABELA ADAMUS, PT
SHELLIE MEKASH, CMT
M'ELLE PIRRI-LEE, PT

This chapter is slightly different than the rest. Three fellow John F. Barnes Myofascial Release (MFR) practitioners, experts, and badass healer friends are contributing to this chapter.

When I imagined putting this book together, it was in part because of the powerful self-treatment tools I've been taught through my MFR courses and experiences. What I know about MFR and what makes having these three amazing women step up to help with this chapter so cool is that there are as many different ways to experience this modality as there are people in the world. There is no one right way to feel a release. So I asked Izabela Adamus, Shellie Mekash, and M'elle Pirri Lee to tackle three different kinds of MFR self-treatment tools here.

Before we get to those amazing stories and tools, it's a great idea to understand fascia, the tissue inside your body that Myofascial Release is based upon. Fascia (pronounced FASHA) is a three-dimensional, head-to-toe system of connective tissue that makes up, surrounds and connects every single cell of every single organ, nerve, blood vessel, muscle, bone, etc...in your body. It is a super-highway for information and energy, a liquid crystalline matrix that plays a role in consciousness.

When fascia is healthy, it can move in any direction and maintains a fluid, mobile state. Fascia becomes dehydrated and/or restricted for many different reasons, including physical or emotional trauma, surgery, injury, inflammation, or repetitive posture. Restrictions in the fascial system can cause serious pressure to build up around the internal structures of your body, which can, in turn, create tightness, pain, and dysfunction.

John F. Barnes Myofascial Release teaches a system of mind-body diagnosis and treatment of fascial restrictions. As practitioners, we learn how to perform these releases on clients and how to educate our clients to perform releases on themselves.

This chapter is broken down into three of those self-treatment techniques; myofascial stretching principles, self-hands-on releases, and small ball (tool) releases,. First, we have Izabela Adamus, PT to help us understand the MFR stretching principles.

# Myofascial Release

STRETCHING PRINCIPLES

by Izabela Adamus, PT

## My Story

Wouldn't it be great if when we are born, we were given that awesome book or manual with detailed instructions on how to live this life? How to find the truth?

And all our questions were eloquently answered like why we are here? What does it all mean? What happens when we die? Why do we get sick? Why do we suffer?

How can we be happy and create the life that we truly want?

But maybe it wouldn't...maybe the thrill of life is to discover it all on our own....in our unique way.

I was definitely this type of curious kid, who was driving my parents crazy with tons of questions about life, existence, death, disease, heaven, and God. I wanted to know the truth about life.

When grandpa died, I was four years old. During the funeral, I felt an overwhelming sense of sadness, pain, and fear as my little mind could not comprehend what happened to my grandpa. He was only 60 years old. It seemed to be that every few years, someone either died or got chronically ill. Uncles, aunts, grandparents, all in their fifties or sixties, just vanished. Somehow I sensed there was something not quite right about that.

*There must be a different way, maybe we don't know something,* I could hear the voice inside of me. A lot of my searching and curiosity, I believe, was coupled with my deep grief, sadness, and confusion related to the fact that between the ages of 4 and 15, I lost five close, relatively young (48-62 years old) family members to various chronic illnesses.

The church was a big part of my early years. I used to love to go to church. I loved to see all my family and friends together, singing and smiling. I had an intuitive sense of God's presence during those times. When I turned six years old, I was told that I needed to come up with things that I "did wrong" and confess them to a stranger regularly. I felt uncomfortable about it. I wanted to be a "good girl" and abide by the rules as it was only external truth available to me, but deep inside, there was a feeling of innocence and playfulness, which in a way others were denying existed.

I remember feeling a sense of been torn inside and not knowing who or what I should trust. That sense of lack of internal trust and not quite knowing what or who to trust followed me for a long time.

As I was getting older, church messages I heard made my stomach feel knotted. I felt uncomfortable in my body hearing messages like, "You were born with sin," and "You will go to Hell if you don't do X, Y, Z." That all made no sense to me. When I became a teenager, I concluded that I was not getting any real answers to my quest for the truth from my church.

My family life was stable and safe, yet preoccupied with trivial daily chores, routines, and superficial living. The more I asked, the more I was told, "This is just the way life is so accept it and come down from the clouds. Why can't you be normal?" I heard this many times.

As I was hoping and craving for wise, mature, deeply connected, and nurturing behaviors and examples around me, life was circling around activities like weekly house cleaning, laundry, and cooking instead. I felt criticized for not fitting in. That was hurtful.

My inner voice would whisper, *there must be more into this life. There must be a different and new way.*

As I observed my life, it seemed most of my growth and maturity came through trials and tribulations, emotional or physical pain, trauma, illness, death, and other unpleasant circumstances. My passion and thirst for the answers led me to read many books about philosophy, psychology, how to reach human potential, religion and spirituality, biology, and how the mind, body, and spirit are connected.

The first time I sensed glimpses of something deeper and real to me was when I was introduced to Transcendental Meditation back in physical therapy school. Right from the beginning, it intrigued and fascinated me. My curiosity was further satisfied when I read *You Can Heal Your Life* by Louise Hay. I started to realize I was finally tapping into something I'd been searching for for a long time but had no idea what it was.

The more I read and enjoyed meditation, the more my appetite grew. I was sensing that I was moving into a much bigger dimension than my five senses could detect or be aware of. I was becoming more excited and exuberant about discovering another way of being, in reference to myself first, and the world around me.

I started feeling more alive, happier, and overall more internally satisfied.

When I was 24 years old, I lost my dad to cancer. He was the young age of 62. A few years later, my only sister's husband died of cancer at the age of 55. Feeling profound sadness and loss in my own heart and the hearts of my family pushed me even deeper into my soul, searching for my purpose. That was a time I felt so hopeless and powerless with the pain, loss, grief, sadness, death, and chronic illness. I wanted to do something about it.

The desire and passion for being the change in the world and for helping others to live a happy and healthy life started to emerge. My road to discovering John Barnes Myofascial Release started with my own pain and dysfunction. I was in my late twenties working as a physical therapist at a local hospital outpatient clinic.

I was very athletic my whole life and enjoyed running, swimming, skiing, dancing, and hiking. I also had what I would consider now a high pain threshold, and I would push through it. I was tough and simply ignored my pain.

When my pain became daily, woke me up at night, radiated down to my leg with occasional tingling and numbness, and started to limit my activity level, I could not ignore it anymore. I felt like I was 90 years old inside my own body. I did not like it! I was afraid of my own future. I was so young and was so unsure about how my future would look. I did not recall any particular injury or trauma, so not taking it too seriously made sense to me.

Diagnostic testing was positive for a right hip labrum tear, and I underwent relatively minor arthroscopic hip surgery, recuperated well, and returned back to work after 6-8 weeks. Even though the severity of my pain was quite diminished, a year after surgery, I was still experiencing a significant amount of regular pain, which I was not willing to accept.

In a synchronistic way, I started noticing different messages, which led me to start taking John Barnes Myofascial Release seminars for healthcare professionals. Since my first seminar in Sedona, I was intrigued, curious, open, and willing to try anything to change my regular pain pattern and learn new ways of looking at things and treating people. From the very start, those seminars were different, we were encouraged to look at every human as a whole and not to view them only as a physical body with different symptoms.

I was learning a lot about the mind-body connection, intuition, awareness, consciousness, energy, and how those parts all play a significant role in overall healing, which is physical, emotional, mental, and spiritual.

I felt like I arrived home. I felt like I belonged there. I started feeling so excited, joyful, and optimistic about my body, my life, and my future.

Within the first two years, I was receiving a significant amount of Myofascial Release treatments myself, and I was taking John Barnes classes regularly as I wanted to learn, go deeper, and heal as much as I could. I was significantly shifting my body and my mind, and my chronic pain was practically gone. I noticed results in both my personal and professional life. I was learning that life does not just happen to me, and I am not a victim of my circumstances. I was learning about energy and how it flows in our biological system. I was discovering self-love and forgiveness and how those spiritual principals can heal our bodies. I was discovering how I wore a mask to cover my true self. And I was learning how to fully feel my body, feelings, and sensations to free myself from the past.

And probably the most important thing I learned was that there is no change without awareness.

In 2004 I made a very clear decision to open my own private physical therapy and Myofascial Release practice. I saw and experienced in myself clear evidence of how the mind-body connection affects chronic pain and life in general. I wanted to create a space where I could spend quality time with people and share a true and authentic way of healing so others could heal not only their body but their life.

Living with chronic pain is not easy or fun. Healing is a process. Those who are fully committed to taking full responsibility for their own body, health, and life know that it takes time. It took me close to two years to heal between receiving treatment and my own self-treatment program, but it was totally worth it! I am 51 years old now, and I look forward to my future with anticipation and no fear.

I enjoy biking, yoga, skiing, and traveling. I compete in Swing and Hustle dancing and can plan my life ahead without fear of how I'm going to feel as I have tools to help me along the way. I'm not saying I don't have any pain at all. As we get older, things are not the same, but Myofascial Release includes many tools to use to help us along the way.

Learning and understanding the principals of Myofascial Release and mind-body connection totally changed my personal and professional life. I'm forever grateful for it and maybe even for my original pain, which took me to places I never thought exist.

It is not a magic pill. Those things do not exist. But if you are ready to take full responsibility for your chronic pain, your life, or want to avoid surgery (I wish I knew about this work before my own surgery), I encourage you to learn about your own mind-body connection. Do not hesitate. Take that first step towards your healing. It will be totally worth it.

It's a journey I didn't even know existed, that changed my life.

## The Tool

There are many powerful aspects of myofascial release. I'm going to share with you the concepts and principals of myofascial stretches or releases in general and then apply it to the head/neck/shoulder complex so you can practice.

Myofascial stretches are more effective than traditional stretches because they address the shortening, dehydration, and solidification (restriction) of the elasto-collagenous complex and ground substance (the components of the fascia).

Holding a fascial stretch for a minimum of 90-120 seconds to engage the fascial barrier is required. And on average, it takes approximately five minutes to release many layers of fascia when there is a restriction. The importance of time is essential for successful and permanent release. During those five minutes, we allow elastin and collagenous fibers to "unstick" and lengthen, and the ground substance to rehydrate.

Back in physical therapy school, we were taught to stretch for thirty seconds, which only addresses the elastic component of the myofascial structures, producing at best only temporary results. Chronic tightness in collagen and ground substance is usually associated with chronic pain and limited mobility.

To simplify this exercise, I chose to walk you through how to correctly apply the stretch release concept to treat your shoulder/neck complex. Most of our modern life requires us to put tension on the upper body, shoulders, and neck. Driving a car or working at a computer causes us to slouch and round our head and shoulders forward. That stress can put tremendous pressure on certain areas producing various symptoms like neck, upper back, shoulder, wrist, and hand pain, carpal tunnel syndrome, headaches, and many more.

- Start off by choosing to work with your right or left shoulder and neck. Sit down with your feet and back supported. Put your arm stretched out sideways, to about 90 degrees, and supported on another chair or a couch. Let's imagine we are creating more space internally between your shoulder and your neck.

- The first thing we will find is the position of stretch or the barrier. Start engaging the barrier slowly by turning your right arm at the shoulder level gently, so your palm is facing up or down. Do it slowly, with awareness and ease, and ask yourself, at what part do I feel the tension? When you find and feel that place, just simply hold it.
- Next, I want you to gently bend your neck to the opposite side of the arm with some rotation until you find the place that feels like it offers you some mild resistance or where you feel a slight tightness. It may take you 90 seconds to find the restriction for that area. Now maintain that for at least five minutes without forcing the stretch.
- As you maintain the stretch, focus your attention on your breath. Breathe in a relaxed way but stay conscious and on purpose. This time is important for collagen to lengthen and for the ground substance to rehydrate. Stay mentally quiet, but be engaged and present with the area you're stretching. Think of it as an active stretch, but your tools are the breath and awareness. Sense it as a relaxed, mental engagement and not force. This will allow you to stay aware and present for the subtle releases, other body parts communicating with you, images, or emotions.
- As time progresses (within a few minutes), you will start feeling softening of the tissue. There might be soreness, but as long as you are sensing the softening and elongation of the tissue, you are doing it correctly. You may sense that your head or your arm want to gently move in different directions. It means your body may go into more spontaneous movement, releasing and unraveling old restrictions. If you are fully present and connected, within a few minutes, you may start feeling gentle movement that happens inside the stretch, which you are encouraged to gently move with. Remember, you are allowing it to happen, not forcing it.

You can use this technique for any self-stretch or release you perform in any area of the body. In the next section, you'll learn how to apply these principles and use your own hands for a deep release of the jaw.

---

**Izabela Adamus, PT, is a holistic physical therapist with over 29 years of experience, an expert level John F Barnes Myofascial Release practitioner and owner of Wholistic Therapeutics,** www.whl-t.com.

**Izabela works with individuals to help them transform chronic pain, promote authentic healing, restore peak function and enhance overall wellbeing. She is always excited and passionate about guiding people on the journey towards self-awareness, optimal health, happiness and applying the healing power of the mind-body connection. Her testimonials attest to the high regard and quality of her work.**

**Izabela combines her expertise as a Myofascial Release practitioner with a holistic philosophy. When combined with her solid scientific medical background as a physical therapist, you are presented with an approach that treats you as the unique whole individual. Izabela's deep belief in every person's internal, healing potential and her desire to ignite and discover it in others, is empowering and helps create resilience in her clients.**

**With over 14 years in private practice, Wholistic Therapeutics' mission is to help clients achieve and sustain optimal levels of function by offering highly specialized, effective one-on-one treatment and many valuable educational tools, and practices. Your health and happiness are the top priorities at Wholistic Therapeutics, where we advocate healing on physical, emotional, mental, energetic and spiritual levels.**

**Izabela grew up in Poland. She graduated from the Academy of Physical Education in Katowice, Poland in 1992 with a degree in Physical Therapy. She's helped hundreds of people and pursued her professional skills in a wide variety of clinical settings in the USA (Michigan, Pennsylvania and Illinois) since 1994.**

**Izabela loves to travel, practices yoga, dance, and participates in a variety of out-door activities. She especially enjoys visits with her family in Poland. Izabela resides and has her practice in the outskirts of Chicago.**

**You'll find more about her programs and sign up for free valuable information here: https://www.whl-t.com/healing-resources.html**

# Myofascial Release

## USING YOUR OWN HANDS

by Shellie Mekash, CMT

We are told in seminar, "Feel beyond your hands." The first time I heard that, I thought to myself, *how in the world do you do that!?* Now I'm telling *you*, yes, you *can* feel beyond your hands! As you sink into the experience, keep an open mind and be curious as to what you feel both in your hands and beyond.

## My Story

Before discovering the wonderful modality that is myofascial release, I'd been on a downward spiral both physically and mentally for several years. Gone were the carefree, blissful days of living in awe and wonder of my four beautiful daughters. Instead, pain, drudgery, and sheer survival were the replacements.

My body systems were seizing up without any real known cause. *How did this happen? How could this happen?* I was scared and confused. Herein lies the beauty of myofascial release therapy. A true mind, body, spirit approach that was nowhere near being on my radar as something that even existed. I felt pride in myself for being a seeker of knowledge and trying to figure out my pain and dysfunction. I reached far and wide to specialists and pain management programs in hopes of finding something, anything, that would help me. Even the world-famous Mayo Clinic! You know you are desperate when you're hoping for a diagnosis, no matter what the diagnosis is, just to have a name or label.

My thought process was if I could name this thing, I could go all-out fight mode and conquer it. I now know that fascial restrictions don't show up on an x-ray, CT scan, or MRI. It makes perfect sense now, but at the time, I knew nothing of the sort. Instead, I had a whole arsenal of prescription medications to combat the variety of symptoms plaguing my body. The pain was incredibly intense and unexplainable to the western medicine folks treating me the best way they knew how. Medications ranged from anti-anxiety to anti-psychotic to anti-seizure to narcotics, all prescribed to help me gain some sort of normalcy and function. But that's far from what happened.

My day would begin by taking Oxycodone just to be able to take a shower and lift my arms to wash my hair. I continued to work, but barely. I would work Monday through Thursday and then come Friday I'd be lucky if by noon I could make my way out to the couch. Recuperating would continue Saturday and Sunday, enough to start the process over for the new week. Evenings would find me in our king-sized bed, sometimes being able to make it to the supper table with the family and often times not. Our girls would lay sprawled on the bed to intimately chat about their day or talk about school or sports. It was a far cry from how I had envisioned my life. We also had a family pact. No asking me or sharing with me any details after I'd taken the evening medications, as I wouldn't remember the conversation the next day.

"Hey, everyone, I'm going to take my meds. Anyone have anything for me before I do?" Imagine my heartbreak when I had to be told by our daughter that she'd called the night before excitedly sharing the news of her engagement, and I had no recollection of the conversation. This was no way to live and not how I wanted our daughters to remember me.

As life progressed, so did the dysfunction in my body. Little did I know what was in store for me.

"Wait, what?" Did I really just hear you say, "You'll have to cath yourself four times a day or be on dialysis for the rest of your life?" As I sat in the urologist's office, numb to any feeling and paralyzed with fear, I heard him say, "I'll send my nurse in to show you how to self cath. You'll get used to it, it's not that bad."

My mind was racing, and my heart was frantically beating out of my chest. *What? Four times a day?* I thought. The nurse came in and proceeded to have me undress from the waist down, showed me the catheter, and then my anatomy markers with a handheld mirror. I stared blankly at her in disbelief. She instructed in a calm, compassionate voice, as I sat there dumbfounded. She then left the room so that I could try this new skill out in private. *What the hell just happened? I have to shove this there?* I thought.

Still unable to process what had just transpired, I remember walking out to my husband waiting in the vehicle for me, carrying a little brown bag. I explained to him the words that had just been spoken to me, in a flat affect. No tears came. I was still frozen in time. My life had just significantly changed.

I never thought this would be the solution to not being able to pee. I fully expected I would be given a pill, and I would be on my way. To go from scoping out venues for bathroom facilities, to now having to plan where and when I would cath myself, took a shift in perspective. I knew I had to embrace this new way of life as I had way too much to live for. The thought of dialysis was terrifying. The doctor had mentioned that there was a new bladder stimulator that I might be a candidate for. "I don't work with those, but you can research it if you want," he said.

Fast forward a few short months, and I was seeking alternative solutions. A sacral nerve stimulator, specifically. This consisted of an electronic device surgically implanted into my right buttock with a lead running internally to the sacral nerves. The basis of this therapy is that the sacral nerves are stimulated via electronic impulses to help correct erroneous or inappropriate messages being sent. In my case, encouraging the bladder to wake up and do its job to release. This worked well for a couple of years, but not without various challenges and long-distance trips to reprogram the stimulator or to undergo lead-revision surgeries.

Little did I know at the time that this shutting down of bodily functions would continue and spread to other systems. Dysphagia and bowel function were soon other areas where my body was locking down in fight or flight response and begging for me to uncover the root cause. Pain surged throughout my body 24/7 without much relief from myriad medications.

I bravely kept seeking solutions. I'd often think, *this couldn't possibly be what the rest of my life would be like, could it?* I had pretty much exhausted all that traditional western medicine could provide me, and the quality of my life was questionable at best. I wasn't living, but merely existing.

Courageously telling my story, explaining all the pain and embarrassing dysfunction yet again to another provider proved to be the best thing I have ever done. I gave it one more shot of being brave, being vulnerable, and sharing my story. Hope wasn't something I freely opened myself up to anymore, as it had been dashed away so many other times. But this time, it felt different. I was met with compassion and an open heart to a different way of thinking and feeling by a local physical therapist that used a different kind of modality. This therapy offered healing in a whole new way that I had no idea existed; mind, body, spirit. What a gift I was given that day! Myofascial Release therapy saved my life and gave my family their mom and wife back.

Through many sessions of MFR, I was compassionately and skillfully guided to allow my body to thaw and release all the past trauma I had unknowingly endured and locked down in the very cells and tissues of my body; layer by layer, belief system by belief system. I experienced a beautiful unfolding of health and return to homeostasis.

What I learned is that the energy of past traumas, physical, mental, or emotional, can be locked in our body in the fascial tissue. And that over time, if not guided to heal or be released, that locked up energy can create very physical problems. Dis-ease. The western doctors were treating my symptoms. Myofascial release finally got to the root cause of my symptoms, the trapped traumatic energy in my body.

If there is an area in your life that you're feeling frozen or fearful, take a leap of faith as I did and seek out a John F. Barnes trained Myofascial Release therapist to facilitate your miraculous healing. There is hope! You, too, can live a life of freedom from pain and dysfunction. Believe me, it is so worth being brave!

In the meantime, take a moment for yourself and explore the benefits of using your very own hands for healing by submersing yourself in the exercise below.

## The Tool

One of the most effective self-myofascial release techniques I teach to my clients is the tempo-mandibular joint release. Releasing the tempo-mandibular joints (TMJ) is fabulous for reducing or eliminating headaches and face, jaw, and/or neck pain, and it can be utilized virtually anywhere.

- To begin, sit in a chair with a desk or table in front of you. Take a deep cleansing breath in through your nose, deep down into your lower belly. Exhale slowly through your mouth. Repeat.
- Slow your breathing, connect with your breath, and begin to relax your head, neck, jaw, and shoulders.
- Now place your elbows on the table or desk with your hands gently resting on the sides of your face. With your fingers resting between your hairline and eye sockets and pointing towards the sky, and your thumbs cradling your ears, maintain gentle pressure on the sides of your face/head.
- Bring your awareness to your fingers and hands and what you are feeling underneath them. Be curious.
- Ask yourself if your skin is warm, or cool, taught, or tingly. Just feel what you feel without judgment.
- Slowly allow your fingers and hands to sink and relax into your face until you feel a little firmness. Stay there for 30 seconds or so, connecting your hands to the sensations in your face.
- Continue to feel into this area. Breathe and relax. What do you notice?
- Now, as you maintain a gentle pressure or compression inward, gently pull your fingers and hands down your face towards the table, letting gravity assist you, without sliding on the skin. Feel this.
- Encourage your body, head, face, and jaw to soften and relax. As you do, you may notice your hands moving down your

face. Allow your hands to gently shift as the tissues adjust underneath them.

- Visualize the tension melting from your tissues like butter melting in a pan or taffy stretching.
- No need to rush. Let it feel good. Stay here for 5 minutes or longer and just breathe.

This release of solidified and stuck fascia takes time. Be patient and easy with yourself. Notice any responses or sensations under your hands and allow and follow any unwinding or movement that may take place under your hands or in your body. You are experiencing the piezoelectric effect, mechanotransduction, phase transition, and eventual resonance or release. Such a beautiful unwinding of stress, tension, and pain!

I encourage you to utilize this tool as often as you identify a stiffness or restriction in your head, face, and/or jaw.

This hands-on release can be performed on many different areas of the body by following the same technique of awareness, relaxation, breathing, gentle pressure, and stretch with a five-minute hold. Let it be easy. For a free audio version of this exercise, visit www.shelliemekash.com/resources.

---

**Shellie Mekash, CMT, is an expert holistic bodyworker specializing in John F. Barnes Myofascial Release, Reiki Master, and dabbler in Qi Gong and Healing Touch. She compassionately helps men, women, and children of all ages achieve relief from chronic pain and stress with a powerful, effective, mind-body approach.**

**Shellie and her husband reside in rural Minnesota on their family farm. She is the mom of four (*yes, four!*) beautiful daughters and five fabulous grandbabies. In her spare time, she can be found supporting their athletic endeavors and soaking in the magnificence of new life and expanding family.**

**Start your journey to health and joy today. Connect with Shellie to begin or dive deeper into your healing journey by visiting her website at www.shelliemekash.com. With awareness, you have a choice!**

# Myofascial Release

## USING THE SMALL BALL AND OTHER TOOLS

by M'elle Pirri-Lee, PT

## My Story

I fell into Myofascial Release by accident. In physical therapy school, I only had a two-hour lecture and a two-hour lab on MFR. While I did find the manual therapy interesting, it didn't fit in with what I had planned after school, so I didn't pursue that interest. I had received a grant from New York State that paid for my last two years of school. In return, I was going to work for a facility that served people with developmental disabilities for at least three years. When I graduated, I went to work at the local ARC. The job was rewarding, and I was happy to stay on after my three years were up.

On September 11th, life changed. A few weeks later, my husband's National Guard unit got called to go down to New York City to provide security for one of the airports. He was away for eight and half days, would come home for one and a half days, then go back to the city. Wash, rinse, repeat. He couldn't call me while he was away, and I had a very hard time not dwelling on my fears for his safety.

Everywhere I went, friends, neighbors, and acquaintances would stop and ask me how he was doing or if I had heard from him. This did not help me keep my mind off his situation.

In order to keep myself from totally losing my shit, I decided to take our dog, Iggy, to agility classes. I'd get out of the house and give myself something else to focus on. He'd done well in puppy kindergarten and several of Iggy's classmates also attended the school's agility classes. Big mistake.

As Iggy and I walked in, the people that knew me from puppy kindergarten all clustered around us, asking for news on my husband, Jim. The people who didn't know me also came over to find out what was going on. I felt ambushed and barely finished the class. I drove home in tears. I lost my shit. I ended up pulling over to the side of the road to finish crying. I had one hand on the steering wheel and my other arm around my dog. I remember sobbing and saying, "Iggy, Mommy's going to find a class to take that is PT related. I won't tell anyone about Daddy, so no one will ask any questions!"

As I got home, I stopped at the mailbox at the bottom of our driveway. There, in with all the other mail, was a brochure for an upcoming myofascial release course, right in Albany. I ran in and tried to call to register, but at that time of night, the office was closed, I had to wait until morning. For the first time in several weeks, I fell asleep excited for the coming day.

The class was amazing. It was taught by John Barnes' son, Brian. He was an excellent teacher, and what I learned changed my life. My brain was engaged in something besides constant worry. I was learning a new and valuable skill, *and* I was finding a way to deal with my anxiety.

At that time, I had a young man as a patient who I had immense difficulty treating. He had spastic Cerebral Palsy, was wheelchair-bound and blind. He had muscle contractures in the back of his legs that were so severe, he couldn't extend either knee to 90 degrees. He had chronic breakdown behind his knees, and nothing seemed to help. The doctor said I wasn't aggressive enough with his range of motion exercises. Whenever I walked into his training room for therapy, he would hear my voice, curl into a tight little ball and cry. We often both ended up in tears.

After taking the course, I began applying the basic principles of MFR to his range of motion sessions: never force, only stretch until you feel the restriction, let time do the work. The difference was astonishing. After five years of tear-filled sessions, he went from crying and curling into a ball when he heard my voice, to laughing and clapping his hands. The breakdown behind his knees cleared up, never to return. He was still in a wheelchair, but by the end of the year, he was able to lift each leg independently in bed to assist his support staff while they were dressing him.

At the same time, my husband's Guard unit ended up deploying overseas. In order to keep my sanity while he was away, I took any JFB MFR course I could find. My skills improved. I loved this new modality. It made such a huge difference in people's lives when I could use it. And it gave me something else to focus on while my husband was away.

I also got treated as part of each seminar. I found areas of my body I didn't realize needed work, areas I had been ignoring. With each class, I learned new self-treatment techniques. I learned how to sink in a little deeper and listen to my own body. Making the time to treat *me* every day made a world of difference. I honestly believe self-treatment was one of the reasons I survived my husband's deployment.

As my own body awareness improved, I found myself noticing areas in other people's bodies, ways they held themselves, that indicated possible fascial restrictions. I remember having to put my hands in my pockets in line at the grocery store to avoid reaching out and touching complete strangers whose bodies had obvious (to me) fascial restrictions. I bullied friends and loved ones into letting me practice on them, and I was able to help so many dealing with pain or limited motion.

By the time my husband got back home, I knew I had to bring this technique to more people. For one year, I saw my own patients two evenings a week after work and on weekends, dragging my massage table into their homes. After building up my own caseload, I took the plunge into private practice and never looked back.

I've now been in private practice for over twelve years, and I have been able to assist so many people on their path to healing. Without exception, the people who make the biggest improvement are the people who practice their self-treatment techniques between sessions with me. I'm so glad I can share this tool with you!

## The Tool

**What you will need:** A quiet space where you won't be disturbed, a surface to lay down on, and to start with, a small ball. A tennis ball will make a good first tool but use what you have on hand. About 45 minutes of your time. (I also find having a selection of my favorite instrumental tunes on hand to be helpful.) If you go back to Chapter 10, you'll find a couple amazing sound healing tracks you can use.

**What to keep in mind:** Releases in the fascial tissues happen slowly. Give yourself permission to take all the time you need for each technique, usually a minimum of three to five minutes.

**The exercise:** Lay down and relax. You can use your bed, your yoga mat on the floor, or just the floor. Close your eyes. Take a few deep breaths. Sink into your body with awareness. Does anything call for your attention? Does something ache? Feel stiff? Sometimes you will locate a troubled or painful spot right away. Do you notice if anything feels hard, hot, or tender?

Position yourself so that the area you have identified is on your bed/mat/floor. Take your ball and place it between your body and the surface you are laying on, right under the area you wish to treat. Roll around a little until you feel the ball in "that spot." Take several deep breaths, get quiet, bring your awareness to the area, urging it to let go or soften. This may be uncomfortable at first. Give yourself several seconds to adjust to the pressure. If after 30 seconds, you are still having trouble tolerating it, try moving the ball slightly away from the area. If it's still too intense, try a more padded surface. For instance, if you are on the floor, try moving to a yoga mat. If the yoga mat is too intense, try your bed. Conversely, if you're not able to locate "your spot," on a specific surface, move to a firmer surface.

Now relax and continue to breathe deeply. As the ball puts pressure into the fascial tissue, you may start to feel a release. It may feel like the area is softening. It may feel tingly, warm, or cold, with any number of changes in sensation. Keep breathing, relaxing, and staying connected to what is happening in your body. Try breathing into the area of restriction. Visualize the area melting, like a pad of butter on a hot slice of toast. As the restrictions release, you may notice a sensation in another area of the body. Make a note of it, but stay on your original spot for a minimum of three to five minutes. The awareness of a connection to another area can tell you where to treat next. After you have felt a few releases, find another spot. Do not force any releases, just allow them to happen. Give yourself permission to let go.

If you can't come up with a starting spot, try a technique I call The Starfish. Lay on your back. Slowly, gently, carefully elongate your neck. Move your head from side to side. Make gentle circles. Sink into your body with awareness. Notice where you feel any discomfort, any place that feels "stuck," and just make a mental note of it. Work your way around your body, doing the same with each limb, elongating, gently stretching each one. Make a note in your head of where you felt areas that may need some TLC. When you have that list, pick one spot and start treating.

If you are having trouble waiting for that three to five-minute time period, try adding music instead of watching the clock. (I keep a playlist of soothing instrumental music, each tune approximately four to five minutes long, to keep myself from cranking my neck around to find a clock or trying to count in my head.) The focus here is tuning into what is going on in your body.

Feel free to experiment. You can try this standing, leaning against a wall with the ball between you and the wall. Try different balls. Different sized balls will fit better into different parts of your body. Areas of your body that are well padded may need a firmer ball than areas that have no padding. Start a collection of balls of different sizes, shapes, and firmness to play with. Approach each self-treatment session with a sense of play and curiosity.

You may find a collection of self-treatment videos at www.adirondackmyofascialrelease.com/video_gallery

## Other useful tools

Once you have mastered the use of the small ball, there are other tools you can experiment with.

The Thumbby, a small, cone-shaped tool created by a massage therapist that replicates the pressure of someone's thumb pressing into your sore spots. This is one of my favorites as it can be stuck on a wall and get into some of those restrictions around the shoulder blade. Find more info at https://www.youtube.com/watch?v=J68R7rGHk14

The CranioCradle, another wonderful small home therapy tool with a multitude of uses. Find more info at https://www.youtube.com/watch?v=l8SIOxBCd7A&t=18s

---

**M'elle Pirri-Lee, PT, is a physical therapist and Expert JFB Myofascial Therapist. With over a decade in private practice, she has helped countless men and women dealing with chronic pain get back in the driver's seat and get their lives back. Her burning desire is to empower women to find help for pelvic floor dysfunction other than buying Poise pads or taking meds. Her office is at 62 Beekman Street, Saratoga Springs NY. If you're sick of being told you have to "live with" pain or dysfunction, reach out to her at 518 225-1440, or melle@adirondackmyofascialrelease.com**

**Facebook at AdirondackMFR.**
**https://www.facebook.com/AdirondackMFR/**
**Website: www.adirondackmyofascialrelease.com**

CHAPTER 18

# Yoga

## Moves for Mindful Pain and Stress Relief

BY MANUELA ROHR, BDY/EY, C-IYAT, PRYT

If I have to name one day in my life that changed everything, it would be the day I became a mother.

Filled with butterflies in my belly of what would come and pictures in my mind of the beautiful faces my little girls and boys would have, I prepared for the right guy and this magic to unfold. I carried this wish in my pocket like a unique, raw diamond I was going to polish soon; an exceptional stone, I thought I would transform into a masterpiece.

My dream broke on a hot summer day in August of 1990. It was the 8th, shortly after 8:00 p.m. Sarina was born four months early by emergency C-section. She weighed 881g (1 pound and 15 oz.) and barely had a chance to live through the night. Her birth followed the loss of three pregnancies. Life taught me early how to be with loss.

Do you have a broken dream? How do you cope?

I had a life before that day, full of dreams, hopes, and possibilities, with a loving husband and at least four healthy kids in tow. Adventures, birthday parties, a house full of laughter, friends, and family celebrations. And perhaps we'd have weddings and grandkids.

And I have had a life after, full of creating new dreams, hopes, and possibilities; a loving husband and one exceptional daughter who cannot live alone. Sarina is on the autism spectrum.

I had to embrace setbacks, tiny steps, different joys, and incredible heartache. We celebrate our family of three but miss not having found a place for Sarina when we are no more.

Hope runs big in my life.

I learned that we need to accept what destiny delivers and turn our sorrows into something meaningful. A few years into being a special needs mom, I found myself at a crossroads. I was exhausted. Everything I said or thought started with worry about my girl. My marriage suffered; I had given up teaching yoga. I needed to ask myself, *who am I besides being a mother?*

I had to look at the missing pieces of my life. And the answer was pointing me in the direction of where I am today. I'm a mother, a wife, but also a healer, my tools are not meant for me alone.

Immersing myself in teaching yoga is healing to me and the people I'm with. It's the joy I felt early on in my career when I was teaching kids who didn't want to move but started to love being active.

The lessons and joy I gather on my mat transform my life. I realized this calling to be a teacher needs to be nourished alongside being Sarina's mother.

Everything changes when a child is born. There are guidebooks or family members who chime in with support. Everything becomes a challenge when the child is differently-abled. You're not celebrating; instead, you're grieving. No books are available, no one can help. It's a lonely world we enter. This unimaginable loss crushed down on me with brutal force and robbed me of the innocent wish I carried in my pocket to have a big family. It taught me how to heal and how to let go and learn new tools to polish my stone.

Every day I remember the next step is always possible.

I had heard people say life is a mosaic, and different pieces find their way into the picture at their own time. But I didn't understand it back then. It's like a diamond; it needs constant polishing to let its brilliance shine. It's our job to grow the patience and deep inner trust to wait for the next piece to find its place to fit the whole picture and to embrace not knowing until it shines. We need to sharpen our awareness of how we do what we do. It's the key to not feel trapped all the time. Awareness is a truth-finder.

Now I understand. Loss is a good teacher.

I loved competitive sports early on in my life. My body was able to move well and fast. I always wanted to teach kids in school and studied to be a Sports and Gymnastics teacher. I loved it. A few kids in my class couldn't follow my curriculum, and I didn't know why. I only knew how to judge from my own experience and how natural my body performed. *Why couldn't they do what was so easy for me and for most others? How could I help them?* I wondered.

A piece of my mosaic needed rearranging. My focus changed. I studied adaptive physical education to understand what those kids needed, and out of the blue, yoga appeared. My view crumbled at first; yoga was much slower than my speedy pace. But slowly, the picture changed; my understanding of what this life is about, who I am, and who I wanted to become moved towards healing.

The most important teaching from then on happened on my yoga mat. Performance dropped away. It was a struggle at first, pushing felt easier than letting go. *Life was happening out there, right?* I thought. No, it happens right here. Now, as you read.

Awareness and self-reflection take time. I realized my life wouldn't stop because I paused. To be still and pay attention to my breath was a different language, but I loved learning it.

The most profound experience happened when my teacher taught me that more is not always better. Surrender didn't mean to give up but to pay attention to what I felt in the present moment.

I was a master in winning with my no-pain-no-gain mentally. I risked injuries, broken bones, yet I kept pushing. I craved the attention, the pats on the shoulder for being a winner.

Now I felt a vast possibility arise. Why would I risk injury after injury? I never felt like I arrived. What I did was never enough.

And the pieces kept coming together. Honoring my body in the present moment was opening the doors to new growth. It's not about the body alone; it's how I show up to myself and the world. This became a new anchor for me of how I wanted to live my life.

It felt like a miracle at the time. Ease was possible. I saw it in my student's eyes when they were able to master a movement that was out of their reach before. Observing them enjoying their body moving brought tremendous joy into my life. But our body can be our teacher if we learn to listen to its message.

And I had a new awareness. I felt a gentleness toward myself. Pushing hard had lost its power. The diamond? I guess you know the answer.

Life is like cooking a meal. You learn different steps. When you burn something, you get a second chance. You start to pay attention. After your first successful meal, you go for more.

You begin by asking, *what would I like to cook?* You get the ingredients and follow the recipe. You brown the onions first, then the garlic, then the carrots, stir it, stay with it, so it doesn't burn. When you start to love this process, the scent is glorious; the melting of the ingredients is a love affair unfolding before your eyes. Love runs high around you when a meal simmers on the stove. I'm never alone in my kitchen and have to keep an eye on the secret snackers!

Getting to know your body is like that. You learn to pay attention to how it moves, how it feels, what it needs, right in front of your observing eyes. Now. Not yesterday or ten years ago. Who would dig up a dish that was sitting on the stove for weeks? Don't do this to your body!

Sitting for six months by the incubator, watching my baby survive taught me everything about how to navigate the bumpy road from suffering to freedom. I sat with her through countless nights, taking refuge in my breath and listening to the whispers in my soul, guiding me to trust and not give up. I don't know how I would have survived without the gifts my yoga practice taught me; this deep connection to myself, the slowing down and most importantly the awareness that I have a choice in how to hold any posture. It became the most important addition for my mosaic and a beautiful way to help my diamond shine.

We can be the victim asking why or accepting what has been given to us. Every cell in our body knows the difference. Our life's message depends on what we choose.

How are you standing in your life? In line in the store? Standing up for yourself in a difficult conversation? Or how about standing next to someone who triggers the hell out of you while all you want is a compassionate heart?

How do you stand with fear, tragedy, and crisis? You can name any situation and check in with yourself about what feelings are present and ask yourself if they're serving you. If not, find out how you want to feel and cultivate that. On our mat, we can learn that skill. Every pose we enter offers a teaching. Do we push more and get greedy? Ask why? Or do we soften and honor what is possible at this moment?

It's a fascinating journey to let things unfold. I still burn sometimes and want to rush; old habits want to win. But year by year, I feel more parts of me melt together. Letting me say yes to the life I have.

My life is guiding me to choose a posture of deep compassion for myself, never putting myself last, but gifting myself time for soulful self-care, so I can share it with others. I know that's how my diamond shines.

Come with me on a simple journey of healing. When you connect your breath to your movements, you enter the present moment.

As we pause in between movements, we get to ask ourselves, *how do I stand in my posture?* The answer gives us a choice, like in life. We can push or let go.

## The Tool

Please read the instructions first before you practice.

Enter a quiet space where you are not interrupted. Wear comfortable clothes, be barefoot or wear socks. Roll out your mat. Have a cushion and blanket handy. Now is the time in your day where you come first!

**1. Gentle warm-up to connect to your body**

- Stand with your feet hip-width apart with soft knees. Bounce a little to make sure you don't lock your knees.
- Put one hand on your chest and one hand on your belly. Notice your breaths touch your hands. With the next inhalation, gently lift your heart to your hand. Keep your chin parallel to the floor; throat soft.
- Let your hands hang by your site. Close your eyes if it feels comfortable. Notice your body standing. Ask yourself: how am I standing up for myself today? Be gentle. There is no right or wrong answer. All you do is be here now.
- Focus on your breath again, and feel how it brings you into the present moment.
- Now imagine you have dipped your arms into cold water, and you're going to shake it off. Have fun, breathe deeply, and shake your arms and hands as vigorously as you like in all directions for a minute or two until you get rid of all the water.
- Pause and let your arms rest again by your site. Close your eyes. Feel the energy in your body now. What has changed? Be curious.
- Breathe deeply but comfortably in and out and open your eyes.

**2. Self-presence exercise and intention setting.**

- Sit on the floor on a cushion or on a chair. Sit upright and relaxed.
- Close your eyes. Become the observer.
- Scan from your feet to your crown like you're going on a journey through your body. Notice if there is any tension and if yes, let it go.

- As you focus on your breath, feel what happens when you inhale and how it changes when you exhale. That's all. Repeat.
- Now focus on your thoughts. What is the first thought you notice? Breathe as you observe. Let what you noticed go with the next exhale. You don't have to figure anything out. Let it all be. All you want to do is paying attention to yourself.
- Ask and breathe between your inquiries. What would I like to receive from my practice today? Reflect. What brought me here in the first place? What posture (attitude) would serve me today? Reflect and create an intention about what you'd like to receive or cultivate. Make a note of your intention on an imaginary piece of paper, tuck it away so you can look at it again later.
- Open your eyes.

**3. Practice connecting breath to movement.**

- Stand up again. Feet hip-width apart. Put your hands in prayer position in front of your chest. Notice breathing in and out.
- Now breathe in and at the same time draw a big circle with your arms out to the side and up above your head. Let your hands come to prayer position way up in the sky. Reach to the ceiling. Look up if you like while you're holding your breath for a few beats, while your lungs are filled.
- Exhale and circle your arms back to prayer position in front of your chest.
- Stand in stillness for a few moments.
- Repeat what you just did three times, then pause again for two breaths to notice your body.
- Become aware when you enter stillness and when there is movement. Remember your intention. Are you practicing in such a way that you create what you'd like to receive?
- Inhale your arms up to the ceiling again and move your

body to half-moon pose to the left (side bend). Imagine you're standing between two panes of glass, so you don't bend forward. Breathe. Inhale back to center.

- With the next exhale, bend to half-moon pose to the right. Inhale back to the center, and with the next exhale, circle your arms back down to prayer position in front of your chest.
- Repeat two more times. Focus on connecting breath and movement.
- Now pause again for a few breaths and feel your body. Honor stillness. How are you standing? What's going through your mind? Stay curious.
- Repeat breathing in with your arms overhead, and with an exhale, start bending forward from the hips with your knees bent. Hang from your hips, so your torso and your arms relax down to the floor. Let your head go. Relax the back of your neck. Let go of doing. Just notice hanging forward, breathing, and letting go.
- With an inhale, prepare to roll your spine up vertebra by vertebra back to standing.
- Stand still and observe your body breathe. Notice the energy in your body while you gently breathe in and out. How are you standing now? Are you standing in your own presence? What do you notice? Let your inquiry go and prepare to sit down.

**4. Integration**

- Sit down. Wrap your blanket around your shoulders to stay warm.
- Close your eyes. Feel your body and breath. Let each breath connect you to the present moment.
- Reflect on your practice. What did you notice about yourself? Breathe. Remember your intention. How did it show up in your practice? Accept what you notice. Let go of judgment. There is nothing right or wrong. Only awareness.

Breathe gently in and out and notice your thoughts. Let each thought go with your exhalation.

- Put one or two hands on your heart center. Feel your hands touch and how your breaths touch your hands. Notice your heartbeat. Connect to your higher self, that place of unconditional love.
- As you gently breathe, ask: What is the most important thing for me in my life today? How do I want to be? Allow the answer to come from your heart, not your head.
- How can I be in my life today to create what I love?
- Sometimes the answer is clear and sometimes not so. Be okay with whatever you notice. Let it be your reality for now.
- Notice your body again. Honor your body for being with you on your journey. Thank yourself for having made time to practice today.
- Open your eyes with the next inhale.

Thank you!

You will find this practice and a collection of videos with short sequences at https://manuelarohr.com/media/

---

**Manuela Rohr is an expert certified Yoga Instructor, a Phoenix Rising Yoga Therapist, and a group facilitator with over 33 years of experience in body-mind healing. She infuses the age-old wisdom of yoga with the therapeutic mindfulness-based practice of Phoenix Rising Yoga Therapy both in Europe and the US, to provide a unique and powerful healing experience.**

**Manuela believes that as long as you can breathe, you can practice yoga. She moves her students toward a life worth living, no matter the obstacles. Life's a balancing act, and Manuela chooses to embrace what's possible every day. She'll show you how to navigate the bumpy**

**transition from suffering to freedom and is committed to living her life with deep joy.**

**Manuela also conquered the extraordinary challenge of raising a special needs child. Her daughter Sarina, 29, is on the autism spectrum. She was born a micro-preemie four months too soon, weighing one pound and fifteen ounces.**

**Manuela calls her daughter her greatest teacher.**

**She works with people who are curious to overcome their limitations in body, mind, and spirit and who want to learn soulful practices to overcome life's impossible challenges. Special needs parents and people who are caretakers at heart are drawn to her her because they know she walked a mile in their shoes.**

**She shares her tools in private sessions and transformational workshops in Germany, the US, and online. She'll teach you what embodied mindfulness means, grow a healthy relationship with your body, engage in self-presence exercises, let go of outdated patterns and beliefs to create new ones that support you every day.**

**Manuela is a co-author of the book *Stories from the Yogic Heart*, and *Winning in Life and Work; Dare to Dream*. Her soon-to-be-published powerful biographical book, *I Cannot Die Until my Daughter Belongs*, documents her path as a special mother, and *365 Tiny Islands* offers soulful self-care practices that help you thrive despite life's challenges.**

**Born in Germany, she now lives with her husband and daughter in Santa Rosa, California. If she is not on her mat or writing, she climbs trees, dances, loves to cook and travel. Find her blogs, book information, and programs at www.manuelarohr.com and join her free Facebook group, where she supports her students to Embrace what's possible!**

CHAPTER 19

# Total Motion Release

## Corrective Movement for Pain Relief and Prevention

BY LAURA DI FRANCO, MPT

## My story

I came across Tom Dalanzo-Baker, the founder of Total Motion Release (TMR), early on in my physical therapy career and learned the basic theory of his corrective exercise system. What I love the most about it is it gives my clients a way to self-diagnose and self-treat their issues, all in just a few minutes of simple movements.

When I first learned this system, I was using it mainly to keep my body in shape for my martial arts practice. A pinchy, sore left hip, and an annoying right-side backache were keeping me from getting to that jumping side kick I loved so much. I've played hard all my life in terms of physical exercise with college soccer, and marathoning in my past. When I began to practice this aggressive full-body combat sport in my late thirties, I started to think, *oh man, I'm getting old, maybe I shouldn't do this kind of stuff anymore.*

TMR not only worked out the kinks and pain, but it also gave me a way to check my body for small issues before they started to create a bigger problem. I'd usually get up in the morning to do my movement checks, but I'd also check again right before a Tae Kwon Do class, to make sure my body was as balanced as possible before we started kicking. During those years of practice, I was peak performing in class and in competitions as one of the oldest women there. And I got excited about teaching TMR to my clients.

As physical therapists and movement dysfunction specialists, we are required by our state licensing boards to take continuing education every year or so. Over a few decades of practicing, one can rack up quite a list of those courses. Total Motion Release has, by far, been one of the most effective, simple techniques I've practiced, one of the easiest to teach my clients, and one of the most complementary systems when combining with other modalities. I'm excited to teach you about it today.

The basic part of TMR I want you to understand is that we're looking and feeling for asymmetries (differences) in the body from the right to the left, in terms of your ability to move. I'll teach you how to check for those differences and then how to treat them to balance them out. These asymmetries (less movement in one shoulder vs. the other, for example) can wreak havoc on your body over time, creating more tightness, and eventually pain. In worst-case scenarios, small problems in the body can lead to things like tendonitis, sprains, strains, or even arthritis.

We all have differences from the right side to the left due to small injuries, repetitive postures, or illnesses that happen over our lifetime. The body is great at compensating to make sure you can function. But over time, those small compensations can lead to bigger ones, and many times, the body can not make up for the differences anymore. That will be the day you feel tightness or pain, or realize you can't do a particular movement anymore.

Total Motion Release can do two things for you; help you catch the small problems before they become big ones, and help to heal a problem that is already big and causing dysfunction.

Corrective exercise through TMR is a system that balances out the asymmetry by exercising one side of the body more than the other. Many of us learned a traditional system of stretching and exercise where we were taught that if you do ten reps on the right, you must do ten reps on the left. Today I'm asking you to have an open mind and realize that not everything you were taught back in PE class was effective when it comes to injuries or other problems in the body. In TMR, I'm going to show you how exercising one side of your body more than the other can greatly speed up healing, improve tightness or weakness, and get you back to doing your regular daily movements and/or exercise or sports routines without pain.

## The Tool

I'll teach you two of the simplest movements in the TMR system: The Arm Raise and The Trunk Twist. When you've mastered the first two, I highly recommend you pop over to www.TotalMotion-Release.com and learn the other two basic movements: The Leg Raise and the Sit-to-Stand.

What you'll need: A surface to sit on where your feet comfortably reach the ground, preferably without anything behind you. Try to minimize distractions while you practice.

What to keep in mind: Body awareness is key for these exercises. Do them slowly and pay attention to what you feel as you move. As an alternative to reading this and then doing it, you might ask a friend to read the steps to you so you can follow along.

Arm Raise Exercise: Sit down with your feet flat on the floor, your posture upright, and your feet and knees pointing forward. The first part of the TMR exercise is the testing portion, where we test each side for movement.

Raise your straight arm, thumb pointed up, up toward the ceiling as far as you can go without bending the elbow or moving the head or neck, and without pain. When you've reached the end of your range of motion, stop and notice how far your arm went. Then lower it back down. Repeat the same thing on the other side.

Which arm could move further or easier? Make a note of that on a piece of paper. And then ask yourself, "My good arm is what percent better than my bad arm?" The arms aren't "good" or "bad," but for the sake of this exercise, we are trying to figure out which one is the better one. Think in terms of small, medium, and large differences. Is your better side zero to thirty percent better, forty to sixty percent better, or seventy to one hundred percent better. Make that note.

Now that we've tested the movement and found your better side, we'll do a corrective exercise or movement on that better side. That will be the only side we exercise.

Now, without worrying about that straight testing position anymore, I want you to raise the better arm up and back, making a continuous effort for about 20-30 seconds or more. Make sure you're breathing and allowing your body to shift and move to make the movement as good and comfortable as you can. This movement portion of the exercise can be a whole-body effort, allowing all the parts of the body to move and shift to help the better arm get the maximum amount of movement it can. Make this a dynamic movement, and if you feel pain, back off a little and soften the areas you feel pain in or stop the motion and try again. The point on the better side is to get maximum action without hurting yourself. Now repeat that same movement one more time on your better side.

Next, you're going to go back to the original testing position we started with and do one test movement on the "bad" side. Slowly raise that straight arm up with a locked elbow to see how far it goes. Note if that movement feels better, the same as before, or worse. We're hoping for better here. Make a note. I'll show you the next exercise now and then explain a little bit about how this works.

Trunk Twist Exercise: Sit down with your feet flat on the floor, your posture upright, and your feet and knees pointing forward. Place both hands, one on top of the other over your belly button. Keep them centered during the entire test. Twist your trunk around to one side as far as you can go without moving your legs. Notice how far you go. Repeat the same thing on the other side.

In which direction could you move further or easier? Make a note of that on a piece of paper. And then ask yourself, "My good side is what percent better than my bad side?" Remember, the sides aren't "good" or "bad," but for the sake of this exercise, we are trying to figure out which one is the better one. Think in terms of small, medium, and large differences. Is your better side zero to thirty percent better, forty to sixty percent better, or seventy to one hundred percent better. Make that note.

Now that we've tested the movement and found your better side, we'll do a corrective exercise or movement on that better side. That will be the only side we exercise.

Now, without worrying about that perfect testing position anymore, I want you to twist your body to the good side, making a continuous effort for about 20-30 seconds or more. Make sure you're breathing and allowing your body to shift and move to make the movement as good and comfortable as you can. This movement portion of the exercise can be a whole-body effort, allowing all the parts of the body to move and shift to help the better side get the maximum amount of movement it can. Make this a dynamic movement, and if you feel pain, back off a little and soften the areas where you feel pain, or stop the motion and try again. The point on the better side is to get maximum action without hurting yourself. Now repeat that same movement one more time on your better side.

Next, you're going to go back to the original testing position we started with and do one test movement on the "bad" side. Slowly twist your trunk to the "bad" side to see how far it goes now. Note if that movement feels better, the same as before, or worse. We're hoping for better here. Make a note. Now I'll explain a little bit about how this works.

If you're sitting there wondering how moving to the better side changed the "bad" side, here's one way Tom described it for me at the beginning that I understood. You know how sometimes you have a kitchen or bathroom drawer that won't open? It's jammed for some reason, and you can't pull it open no matter how hard you pull? And if you pull any harder, you know you'll bust the drawer even more? And sometimes you have to push the drawer in the other direction and jiggle it, getting it on its track, so that it will open easily? Good side movement is like that. It's the movement we have to do to jiggle, release, and open up our system so that it will move better. The problem with traditional exercise is that you're typically taught to do an equal amount of repetitions on both sides, no matter what. In the TMR system, doing reps on the "bad" side over and over again would be like busting that drawer. So we do movement to the good side to balance things out first. Once the system is more balanced, exercise movements can be done on both sides without risking more injury.

If you're intrigued by what happened in your own body as you followed along, I highly suggest you visit www.TotalMotion-Release.com and watch a few of Tom's videos now. He has some amazing resources to help you learn the full system and take this to another level.

---

**Laura Di Franco, MPT is the owner of Bodyworks Physical Therapy, a private practice in Bethesda, Maryland, founded in 2008. With thirty years of expertise in holistic healing, she'll coach you through corrective exercises that make a difference, helping you reduce pain, and prevent injuries. Contact her to make an appointment at www.BraveHealer.com or by email at bodyworkspt@comcast.net.**

## CHAPTER 20

# Toning

## The Magic in Your Voice

### BY SHARON CARNE

It happened again! Ear-to-ear grins, eyes sparkle, shoulders drop, jaws relax, breathing deepens, playfulness twinkles, hearts connect, and peace fills the room.

My being fills with purpose and glee whenever I'm invited to share with others how deeply they're wired to respond to sound and music. And my being fills with awe every time people remember their intimate connection and profound response to sound.

Oh my! What a journey to arrive here! Have you ever made a promise to the universe?

Twenty years ago, I stood on top of one of the hills in our city and declared aloud this promise to the universe from the depths of my soul, "I promise that I will walk the journey my soul wanted to walk in this lifetime. I do not know what that journey is, I just want you to show me the next step."

Never in my wildest dreams could I have imagined the journey my soul had in mind for me. Living my promise has completely transformed my life and my work.

I have been a musician, a classical guitarist, all my life, and for thirty years was blessed with a successful career at the Conservatory at Mount Royal University, sharing music with the hearts of so many young (and young at heart) people. This work filled my heart with joy!

What a surprise to discover, and then to accept that this work was actually preparation for the deeper work yet to come. After my promise, the journey intensified.

The first eight years was a deep dive into the deepest corners of my own psyche. As I carved away at beliefs and patterns, I made more and more room for the infinite soul walking this journey with me.

My heart then pointed me to the ancient and healing nature of sound. For years, my feet wore deep paths to the library, bookstores, and then to studying with pioneers of sound healing and sound therapy. Every fiber of my being knew I had come home to soul work.

Twelve years ago, a new stepping-stone appeared as a phone call from the Director of the Integrative Health Institute at Mount Royal University. She asked me if I would create a program as a facilitator in a study on stress the Institute was sponsoring. They wanted to explore the effectiveness of sound therapy in reducing stress.

With delight, I created a program and shared it with the people in my group. On the final day, they surrounded me with questions about how to learn more. I had no answer for them and knew I had to create one. Sound Wellness was born a month after that.

Oh, there are so many delicious stories I could share with you! But they are for another time. Here, in this chapter, we create sacred space for the magic of your own voice.

One of the most powerful healing tools you have is within you. When you combine your own voice with the brilliant focus of your conscious intent, you have in your possession the clay from which to sculpt miracles.

Your voice creates sound. So let's jump into some basics about sound.

Sound is defined as vibrational energy. It is very physical energy that can move matter itself. It's one thing to say this. It's another thing to feel and see it for yourself.

Please check out the resource page for "The Magic in Your Voice" to view my video on our YouTube channel. www.soundwellness.com/magic-in-your-voice Watch the sound of my voice moving sand into beautiful patterns.

Not everyone knows that sound goes through you. In fact, it goes through you faster than it goes through the air. As an energy source, sound has to push against atoms and molecules in order to move, including your atoms and molecules.

As sound travels through you, it sets every atom into a state of vibration. Now, if the source of the sound is a jackhammer, the vibration created within you can be quite jarring. If the source of the sound is a beautiful mountain stream, the vibration created feels like ahhhh...

Sound is food for your nervous system. We all know that there is junk food, good food, and superfood. It's the same with sound. Junk sound, like the jackhammer, stimulates your nervous system to release hormones that create the stress response. Good sound, like the mountain stream, stimulates your nervous system to release hormones that create relaxation.

Super sound is where your voice shines. Every sound you make with your voice moves every atom of your being. Granted, the voice can be very much like junk sound. It can also bring you the benefits of good sound.

Super sound created by your own voice and amplified with your conscious intention is a match made in heaven for your nervous system and your entire being.

One way the voice creates super sound is called Toning. This super sound literally gives your entire being a sonic massage from the inside out. It massages your body into harmony and balance, calms the emotions, and aligns you with the deepest essence of your soul.

Toning can be described in two ways:

1. The natural voice of the body.
2. A singing sound on a vowel sound or other simple sound.

## 1. Toning as the Natural Voice of the Body

The natural voice of the body comes from the body rather than the mind. We use the natural voice of the body all the time. We just don't call it toning.

Your voice carries every frequency of your body. You have it with you all the time, and it costs you nothing to use. Consider the sounds that flow naturally from your body without even thinking about it:

"Ahhhh, what a cute puppy."
"Ahhhh, that feels good."
"Ooooo, how interesting."
"Ooooo, I like that."
"Uhh, that's heavy."

Can you imagine how much more it would hurt when you stubbed your toe if you didn't say, "Ouch!?" Moans and groans are other sounds that come from your body instinctively.

All of these natural sounds of the body actually stimulate your nervous system to release neurochemicals and endorphins that help your body heal or manage pain.

Here are two exercises on how you can use the natural sounds of your voice to amp up the healing release of endorphins and also to help minimize symptoms of stress.

## Exercise 1: Relaxation as Simple as a Sigh

You can use the natural voice of the body to discharge excess emotional energy and the stress it brings on. We do it all the time. We sigh. We just don't do it consciously.

A good sigh is one of those natural sounds of your body that stimulates the brain to release endorphins that create relaxation. A vocalized sigh is even more useful. A vocalized sigh is when you actually say, "Ahhh" as you sigh.

To maximize the effect of the sigh and the release of endorphins, start the vocalized "Ahhh" around the middle of your vocal range and let it drop into the low sound of your voice as you sigh "Ahhh" on a long full breath.

Try it three times. Notice how you feel.

I have shared this experience with thousands of people, and most often, I hear, "I feel calmer!" or "I feel so much more relaxed!" What you are experiencing is the release of endorphins, the "feel good" hormones dissipating the stress hormones, adrenaline, and cortisol.

## Exercise 2: Be Here Now

Many of us spend most of our day in our heads! Maybe you are working on a report due tomorrow at work, sitting in a brainstorming session, in a community meeting, solving problems, cooking dinner, driving kids to activities, or the worst one—captured by ongoing chatter in your mind, especially the worry chatter.

The truth is, you do your most effective and greatest work when you are grounded and present. One of the sounds you can use to ground and become more present instantly is the word HO. This strong, quick sound comes from deep in your belly after you have taken a deep breath. Try it three times. Remember, it needs to be a very strong, low, and quick sound.

How do you feel? Do you feel more present, more focused? HO grounds you into your body, allows your mind to clear, and you to become more present.

## 2. Toning as a Simple Singing Sound

Toning is also the use of a singing sound to create an even greater effect. This is simply singing an extended vowel sound on the breath.

So let's ramp things up a little!

## Exercise: Ramping Up Super Sound: Toning for Chakra Health

As you tone, I recommend the lowest sound your voice can make for the root chakra, gradually getting higher with each chakra to the highest sound your voice can make at the crown chakra.

The intention of this exercise is to clear and balance each of the chakras. Find a quiet space where you can do this exercise undisturbed.

Caution: Please do not do this exercise when you are engaged in any activity that requires your focus or concentration. This exercise can make you feel quite ungrounded by shifting you to deeper brainwave states.

## Check Within:

Before you begin the toning, check in with yourself right now. Are you feeling a little tired or energized? Check in with your body, your emotions, your mind, and your spiritual connection. Record your observations in your journal.

Decide how many times you will tone the sound for each chakra. I recommend three to seven times for each chakra. Sound is a powerful and transformative work. Remember to care for yourself and practice with moderation and gentleness.

This system of vowels and chakras was created by Jonathan Goldman in 1986. It has become the most widely used system in North America and is easy to learn.

Let's begin.

## Create Sacred Space

Light a candle, say a prayer, tone three OMs or ask for the presence of sacred beings. Remind yourself of your intention and begin the toning.

## The Root Chakra

The sound is *UH*, as in "hug."
The Sacral Chakra
The sound is *OOO*, as in "shoe."
The Solar Plexus Chakra
The sound is *OH*, as in "flow."
The Heart Chakra
The sound is *AH*, as in "mama."
The Throat Chakra
The sound is *EYE*, as in "sky."
The Third Eye Chakra
The sound is *AYE*, as in "hay."
The Crown Chakra
The sound is *EEE*, as in "see."

## Silence

Sit in silence for a few minutes when you finish toning for the crown chakra.

## Grounding

Following this exercise, it is essential to ground back into everyday consciousness. To do this, tone as below with the intention of grounding back into everyday awareness.

- tone one breath on eee for the crown chakra.
- tone one breath on aye for the 3rd eye chakra.
- tone one breath on eye for the throat chakra.
- tone one breath on ahh for the heart chakra.
- tone one breath on ohh for the solar plexus chakra.
- tone one breath on ooo for the sacral chakra.
- tone THREE breaths on uhhh for the root chakra. Wiggle your toes as you make the UH sounds.

Now, please take a moment to check within. How are you feeling? Do you notice a difference between how you felt before you began the toning and how you feel now? Record your observations in your journal.

Are you curious about turning up the miracles in your voice to full volume?

Tone with people from around the world as we co-create ear to ear grins, eyes sparkling, shoulders dropping, jaws relaxing, breath deepening, playfulness twinkling, hearts connecting, and peace in every cell. Join me live on Sunday evenings for my weekly chakra toning on the Sound Wellness Facebook page. Please go to the Resource page for the link: www.soundwellness.com/magic-in-your-voice

As you explore the many wonderful ways to connect with that brilliant spiritual self of yours, you begin to notice that you are bringing happiness, health, harmony, hope, humor, and passion into your life.

When you notice this in yourself, you will begin to notice that there is a quiet song flowing from many hearts, a song of connectedness. And from this place, we begin the song of a new way of being for all of us.

From all of my heart, I wish you the following blessing:

May you be well.
May you be happy.
May you dance with abandon.
May you always live with a song in your heart.

Music has been part of Sharon's life from singing in church choirs as a youth, formal music study on the classical guitar in her teens and earning a Bachelor of Music Degree from Queen's University, Kingston, Ontario and a Master of Fine Arts Degree from the University of Minnesota, Minneapolis, Minnesota in guitar performance. In 1988, Sharon was invited to join the faculty of The Conservatory, Mount Royal University in Calgary, Alberta, where she pioneered the teaching of classical guitar to young children for almost 30 years.

Sometimes the universe has other plans. Her curiosity about the deeper and healing nature of sound was sparked by some innocent exercises in stage fright with some nervous adult students in the early 1990s. This led to intense personal research in sound healing and sound therapy and ultimately to study with two of the field's pioneers, Jonathan Goldman and Tom Kenyon.

As soon as she landed there, Sharon knew she had come home to soul work.

In 2008, she was invited to participate as a facilitator in a study on stress reduction sponsored by the Integrative Health Institute at Mount Royal University. She developed a program specifically for the study using a variety of ways sound and music relieves stress. At the conclusion of the program, enthusiasm was so high that the material was expanded, and the Sound Wellness program was created to bring this valuable information to a larger audience.

Sharon's soul work has evolved with the creation of the Sound Wellness Institute and, more recently, co-founder of the Emergent Workforce Program. Through the Sound Wellness Institute, holistic health practitioners receive the highest level of competency training in Canada in using sound and music to support their practice. Recently, Sound Wellness practitioner training received full approval from the Natural Health Practitioners of Canada Association.

The Emergent Workforce program is dedicated to restoring wellbeing, community, purpose, creative collaboration, and kindness to the workforce while supporting the financial goals of the organization. When we are making a purposeful contribution, our lives are filled with passion, creativity, inspiration, compassion, and wellbeing.

You are invited to explore our websites at www.soundwellness.com, and if you are interested in our programs, visit www.soundwellnessinstitute.com and here is our resource page: www.soundwellness.com/magic-in-your-voice

CHAPTER 21

# Sound Healing

## Healing with Frequency Minded Music

BY IAN MORRIS

Music is both mathematical and magical. It can touch so many different people in so many diverse ways. My name is Ian Morris, and I am a Sound Alchemist and the founder of Listening to Smile. In this chapter, I will explain what Frequency Minded Music is and why the benefits for you can go even further than what traditional music has to offer. But first, I would like to share a little about me and the story of what has brought us together in the healing power of sound.

In 2012 I was in a pretty unhealthy spot. I weighed in at 312 pounds, and I was suffering from a whole plethora of health issues from chronic migraines, heart palpitations, autoimmune and digestive issues, severe depression, and daily anxiety. I had lost all hope and trust in my body. I played sports and was active for most of my early life and never had to deal with health issues to this degree. I spent the next year in and out of the emergency room and making my rounds to different specialists. After a year of doctors' visits, I was ultimately diagnosed with MS and colon cancer. Being an artist and musician at that time, I was uninsured and overwhelmed at the cost of the road ahead. After spending thousands of dollars at doctor's appointments over the year, there was no way I could afford the necessary treatment to recover. I was angry, I was frustrated, and I was scared as Hell.

The mainstream approach was not working for me, so I began actively seeking answers through books, documentaries, conversations with family and friends, and a deep study of online resources about mindfulness techniques and holistic-based options. That road brought me to some really great information that inspired me to start a daily self-care practice that included meditation with Frequency Minded Music, breathwork, and intention setting. When I first started with these self-care practices, I wasn't very good at them. I was never a person that could sit still. I was always daydreaming about my next creation as an artist or overthinking the meaning of life. I was a busy bee, with a very active mind.

As soon as I introduced headphones into my daily meditation practice with Frequency Minded Music, I was blown away at how powerful it was in helping to step my mind down to a more relaxed state. It helped to ease my anxiety and helped my body find peace and rest for the first time in my life. I quickly learned that healing is a multifaceted approach. From that point forward, I started studying nutrition and food combinations that supported my self-care practice on an even deeper level. This created the perfect, whole body balance approach to my healing journey.

In a year's time, I lost over 100 pounds and started seeing major changes in my dyslexia, focus, and creativity. The changes were so radical that most of my friends and colleagues were so amazed that they started to ask me what I was doing and wanted to try it for themselves. This eventually led me to establish my company, Listening to Smile. I wanted to be able to share what I'd learned with people all over the world that felt hopeless (like I did) on their healing journey.

## What is Frequency Minded Music?

Frequency Minded Music is a conscious intention to introduce you to a consistent frequency or tone that has proven to be useful in facilitating a certain mood, feeling, or brainwave state. Unlike traditional sound therapies (EX: tuning forks Therapy, Vibro-acoustic Therapy, Gong Therapy, and Singing Bowls Therapy), Frequency Minded Music incorporates various melodies that are introduced throughout the duration of a song. These additional melodies/frequencies are tuned in the same note or key of the healing foundation frequency.

The goal of Frequency Minded Music is to engage and entertain while providing the listener with a specific intention to focus on throughout the experience.

Frequency Minded Music utilizes science-backed methods that deliver a constant frequency of healing for the duration of the song. Frequency Minded Music tracks are composed with vibration in mind, meaning that they focus heavily on bass and the lower end frequencies of the instruments in the song. This is an important part of the composing process because our physical bodies respond in a powerful way to lower frequencies (20Hz—400Hz). They are soothing and very grounding, which makes them ideal for relaxation and meditation. The lower frequencies hold the foundation and engage the body. The combination of both the higher and lower frequencies, in the form of harmonics and octaves, is what facilitates the process of real breakthroughs. This helps the physical body feel safe and supported while challenging the mind and the ears to grow beyond the mundane routine and the same old sound palette that we are exposed to each day. If working out at the gym builds muscle for the body, then working with sound and intention is the exercise that builds a clear and focused mind.

Frequency Minded Music is a merging of two worlds: the upbeat and emotional side of traditional music with the science of sound healing. The traditional sound healing tools and instruments hold down the root of the song with tone, tuning, or frequency. Once I have the frequency laid out in the song, I'm free to explore the endless combinations and possibilities of melody, tempo, and mood for the intention or focus that has been selected.

## How Frequency Minded Music Can Help You Heal

As with most things in life, consistency is the key. In this section, I will cover the tools and plan for consistently incorporating Frequency Minded Music into your daily self-care routine for healing.

I have seen it time and time again, people having powerful breakthroughs in their healing and release work with Frequency Minded Music. The amazing part about this is that reaching these breakthroughs does not take a huge commitment of time. All you need is the desire to heal and dedication to the daily consistency of your meditation practice. Just 20 minutes a day is all it takes for many of our clients to find relief with their targeted issues in the first week. If you put in the work, you will see the benefits. Frequency Minded Music is even easily paired with other modalities and self-care practices, so it makes it easier to fit into your daily routine. Below are some examples of how you can integrate Frequency Minded Music into daily mindfulness practices.

## Suggested Mindfulness Techniques

Using Frequency Minded Music in tandem with these powerful mindfulness techniques for just 10 minutes in the morning and 10 minutes in the evening is all you need to create powerful ripples of change in your life.

**1. Focus and intention**

When I speak of focus and intention, I want you to get clear and truthful with yourself about where your problems lie and get deep into what healing really looks like for you. This is the first step in working with frequency as your thoughts, focus, and intentions are the steering wheel for these powerful vibrations!

**2. Deep Listening**

Deep listening is truly a lost art in today's world of hustle and bustle. Deep listening is a complete focus on a music track with no multitasking. Get personal with the music as you're on this sound journey. See if you can pick out the different types of instruments and their different separate melodies. Feel the feelings that wash over you and observe, observe, observe.

**3. Breathwork**

There are many types of breathwork, but we are going to focus on one simple exercise.

I suggest doing at least 3 to 5 of these breaths before starting the meditation and continuing this breath as you are able during the duration of your meditation. This exercise is very simple but powerful, and definitely effective. To start, breathe in for a count of five, then hold the breath for a count of five, and finally exhale for a count of 5 seconds. If you were unable to do a count of five, do what is comfortable and work your way up, or increase the count to a higher number.

**4. Visual Imagery / Manifestation**

The mind is a powerful tool and ally in your healing journey. The goal of visualizations is to help the mind make a connection with your focus and intention. So, for example, you would visualize the healthy body and positive outcomes you desire on your healing journey. You would also focus on the type of powerful and positive manifestations you were looking to incorporate in your life. The most important part of visualizing is to feel it as though it has already happened. What would it feel like to reach your goal! What would it look like to reach your goal!

**5. Movement Meditation**

Movement meditations utilize Frequency Minded Music in tandem with physical activities such as hiking, biking, yoga, walking the dog, dancing, or any of your favorite ways to move your body. These tracks are typically composed of mid-tempo or upbeat styles and are shorter in duration. They have a heavy focus on rhythm and more energy than the deep meditation tracks. For examples of these songs, please visit our website at listeningtosmile.com

**6. Creative Journaling**

I have found it extremely helpful in my own personal meditation practice to journal after each one of my meditation sessions. This creates a healing timeline that can help me keep track of my progress and provide huge insights into the healing that may get overlooked. When I journal, I write down any visions or feelings that come up for me during my session as well as any colors, smells, or words. I also write down my overall feeling at the end of each session, and sometimes this includes any creative inspiration such as frequency, songs, poems, and so forth.

So now that we have covered the basics let's give it a try!

What you will need:

- An open mind
- Quiet Space
- A pillow, yoga mat, blanket, and anything else you need to get comfy
- Over-the-ear headphones—(For receiving the highest possible benefits, playback of the Frequency Minded Music tracks is not recommended for phones or laptop speakers)
- Music playing device such as an iPod
- Frequency Minded Music tracks (loaded onto your music playing device or streaming from the web)

Before you begin, find a quiet, warm, and safe space. Make sure you have your over-the-ear headphones and music playing device (such as an iPod) with you before you begin.

Take a seat on a comfy cushion, pillow, yoga mat, or blanket, whatever you have available. This can be on the floor, a chair, or even lay down.

1. Take a few moments and get in tune with your body. Close your eyes. Connect with your senses. Feel the space around you. Smell the scents in the room. Listen to the sounds near

you. Swallow a few times to bring awareness to the taste and sensations in your mouth. Connect with your core self through the senses. Take your time.

2. Now notice your breath. Come into the breath. Notice the cool air coming into the nose through your inhale and the warm air as it exits the nose on the exhale. Take a deep inhale. Exhale out completely. Inhale. Breathe it all out. Another inhale and slowly empty the lungs.
3. Place your headphones on and get the Frequency Minded Music track ready to play. Before hitting the play button, set your intention for this meditation. It can be a word or a sentence or a thought on something positive and uplifting that you are focusing on for your life.
4. Now with your eyes closed, draw your senses into the middle of your forehead, the third eye. This is the point of spiritual realizations. Focus here. Breathe. Take all energies and send them to this central area between the eyebrows.
5. Press play on your music playing device and keep the eyes close and keep the breath slow, long, and calm. Listen to the complete track or at least 10 minutes at a time, or longer if you feel compelled.
6. At the end of the track, sit in stillness as you continue to breathe strong and calm. Stay here for at least a few minutes to allow the body and mind to come back to this reality. Follow up with the long deep breathing exercise that I explained in the last section.
7. Practice this meditation for at least 10 minutes in the morning and 10 minutes in the evening before bed.
8. Journal about any experience you had during and after your meditation. Continue to journey throughout the week. Pay close attention to your feelings, thoughts, visualizations, and events that you encounter afterward. Sometimes, it's the smallest, most subtle things that we often miss, but it can be these things that play a large part in our healing journey.

## Frequency Minded Music

Here is a link to two MP3 tracks to get you started: https://listening-tosmile.com/chapter21-resources/

390.6Hz is a custom frequency by Listening to Smile that we have named "The Frequency of Peace" and works to relax the body and mind. This is powerful fuel for your targeted intention.

528Hz is from the Solfeggio Scale and is called "The Frequency of love."It works with the solar plexus chakra and helps with anxiety relief, pain relief, weight loss, and reprogramming the brain.

These tracks are for PERSONAL USE ONLY and are protected by copyright laws!

If you're interested in using our music in your holistic based business or practice, we offer a membership program that provides you with:

- New monthly Frequency Minded Music
- Training on how to integrate Frequency Minded Music into your established business
- The proper music licensing permissions in your business
- Ability to resell the music to your clients for a commission
- Ability to utilize the music in your advertisements and promotions on social media.
- Support via email and phone for as long as you are part of our team

To learn more about our Sonic Meditation Affiliate Program, visit this link: https://listeningtosmile.com/meditation-affiliate-program/

**Ian Morris Sound Alchemist, Multi-instrumentalist, Poet, Visual Artist, Author, and Intuitive Healer, Founder of Listening to Smile https://listeningtosmile.com – Healing Frequency Minded Music for Personal Growth and Wellbeing**

**Ian has over 21 years of experience in the performing arts field and has made it his life's goal to use his gifts and passion to be of service to people in search of healing. His career started at Interlochen Center for the arts in Interlochen, MI. Shortly after that, he founded a nonprofit called Homemade Genius, where he worked in the underserved community with music and art lessons as well as after school programs. He also worked tirelessly to bring music and art into nontraditional venues in and around the community. He worked with other organizations such as Meals on Wheels, Hospice, and The United Way to use music as a tool for release and healing. After seeing the amazing results, Ian wanted to go deeper into the healing power of sound, which led him down the path of holistic options paired with mindfulness techniques. He started meditating daily with frequency, breathwork, and intention setting.**

**His healing method quickly grew into the beginning stages for his company Listening to Smile, which he founded in November of 2016. Today Listening to Smile is international! Ian runs Listening to Smile with his partner, Dana Kato, where they are growing awareness for Sound Healing and working as true pioneers in the field.**

CHAPTER 22

# Essential Oils

## Shift Your Mood & Energy with Scent

BY BONNIE CHASE, RN

In 2010, I was working as a nurse manager. What I thought was my dream job turned out to be a slow downslide into rock bottom. I was constantly trying to keep the nurses happy and take care of their needs. I had three doctors that didn't get along with each other, and I tried to meet their requests about how the clinic should operate. I was under pressure to meet the financial goals of the hospital, and I felt like the dollar became more important than the patient. I was caught between implementing hospital rules, staffing guidelines, doctors' demands, and nursing needs. Not an easy task. I spent my days at work trying to satisfy the needs of everyone, but that was an impossible task. I was an expert at putting out fires and pacifying people. Each day, I lost another piece of my soul.

On the outside, I had a life others envied. I had a nice little suburban house, a new SUV, great kids, a nursing job that other nurses envied with too-good-to-be-true hours, and a great marriage. But on the inside, I felt like dying. I often thought things like, *I'm exhausted, I have no energy, my knees hurt, my brain is foggy, I'm depressed, and I'm fat!* I'd gained 80 pounds. All I did was work, eat, and sleep. You know, the proverbial mouse on a hamster wheel. I felt like a robot just going through the motions each day.

I was raised in a religious household where the woman's job is to stay at home and take care of her family, especially her husband. So being a dutiful wife, I took care of everyone's needs when I came home. Even though I was exhausted from work, I walked in the door to cook dinner, do the dishes, toss in a load of laundry, do one or two cleaning chores, help my daughter with her homework, and be the perfect wife to my husband.

One evening I came home from work after a long, stress-filled day. I walked into the living room and flopped down into the overstuffed recliner chair. My brain was mush. I was mentally and physically exhausted. I had no desire to move. I was tired, no, I was exhausted. My energy was as low as it had ever been. My husband was out in the yard, mowing the lawn, so, fortunately, I had the house to myself.

As I sat there, I tuned out my home life. I just couldn't do another thing for anyone. I went on an internal tirade with God. *I can't keep doing this. Life is supposed to be good. I need a change. I hate my job, but I'm stuck. I'm working so hard, and this is all you can do for me? What the fuck is this life all about? I'm miserable. Why am I here? Is this all there is to life? I'm sure there's got to be some reason I'm here in this life, and I sure wish you'd let me in on what it is because this life isn't worth living. And where's my winning lottery ticket? I do everything I'm supposed to, and here I am, miserable! What the fuck!?* I had reached my rock bottom.

After my tirade with God, I sat there thinking about what was going on, and I let my thoughts wander. I felt the presence of one of my spirit guides, Merlin. I heard his voice as if he was standing next to me, the words flashed through my mind. *It's time for magic.* The voice was so loud and clear, I looked to my left and expected to see him standing beside me. He wasn't. I thought to myself, *what the hell does that mean, it's time for magic?* I sat for a moment and then I felt an energy flow through me. Merlin gave me the answer through thought. *You have to change to have what you desire. You are not a victim of life but of the experiences you allow. It is time you take care of yourself. You must value yourself above all others. The life you seek is yours to create.*

When I opened my eyes, I felt different about my life. I had a new perspective, a new knowing. I felt refreshed and empowered. I felt a renewed energy for life. I had some hope. There was a shift inside me, I had a purpose. I had practiced listening to my intuition before, but this was different. I had a strong knowing that didn't exist before. I just knew deep inside what to do. Self-care and following my intuition became the foundation on which I rebuilt my life. I had to learn to say no to others and yes to myself. I was responsible for creating my own magic. I could create my own life.

I'd been searching for myself and my purpose for a long time. I was confused and hopeless, but with this message from Merlin, I felt new clarity. I realized I had to lose myself to find myself. After that night, I found my voice, I started to speak my truth, and my life began to heal. I read every self-help and personal development book I could. I took classes and workshops, and I practiced listening to my body. Slowly my body began to heal from dis-ease, and I discovered a newfound sense of purpose.

My life was about finding the lessons in my pain, creating joy from my experiences, and breaking free from conformity and complacency. I began to reconnect with the sacred feminine essence within and honor my body and her needs.

My transformation began by taking care of my body through radical self-care. One of the tools I used was essential oils. A friend introduced me to essential oils, and through my research, I started to understand about the energetic and vibrational properties of the oils. I began using them at bedtime and noticed a huge difference in my sleep right away. My sleep felt more restorative, and when I woke in the morning, I felt refreshed. The other powerful way I began using the oils was to create a ritual for myself that helped me change negative or anxious thoughts to positive, more healthy thoughts. When I did this regularly, I felt more confident and empowered. My old negative beliefs simply dissolved, and my self-worth began to strengthen.

I'm passionate about holistic health and healing, so I looked to Mother Nature for answers, guidance, and natural medicine. Essential oils were medicine for me throughout my healing journey and helped to raise my vibration.

## The Tool

### USING ESSENTIAL OILS TO SHIFT YOUR MOOD

When you look at the science here, what you'll learn is that scent is one of the most powerful senses you can use to alter your emotions, mood, and body physiology. Aroma is first a neurological response at the olfactory nerves. Then a chemical signal is sent to the hypothalamus gland, which stores and creates a memory. The signal then moves into the pituitary gland and finally into the endocrine system, where a neurochemical response is produced that governs the systems of the body. At the same time, the chemical response from the hypothalamus gland sends a signal into the amygdala, which controls our emotional center and creates a neurochemical response that governs our emotions.

Everything has a vibration, including the food we eat, the people we surround ourselves with, and our thoughts. Essential oils are one of the highest vibrational substances you can use on your body, which helps to elevate your overall energy field and help you feel your best. So be aware of your space and choose the highest vibrational surroundings to lift you up. Essential oils are the essence or fragrant parts extracted from the plant using water or steam distillation or cold-pressed methods. The resulting oils are highly concentrated and up to 100x stronger than the natural plant. A little goes a long way when using essential oils. Essential oils smell great, but they are beneficial to our physical body and mental wellbeing.

Here's what essential oil expert, Andrea R. Warren had to add about the benefits of using oils:

"Essential oils and their powerful scents can overpass sections of the brain that our other senses cannot. This gives them the capability to tap deep into the limbic system allowing us to release emotions, old habits, and limiting beliefs. Once we connect our new belief or mindset to a particular essential oil, whenever we feel overwhelmed, we only need to breathe in deeply to recalibrate and get ourselves back into alignment."

~ Andrea R Warren AIA, CHWC, CABC

The two most common ways to use essential oils are by inhaling them or applying them directly to the skin. Inhaling the essence of the essential oil will work quicker while applying the oils to the skin will be slightly slower in effect, but the benefits will last longer. Both methods work well.

## Inhalation Method

When you inhale an essential oil by holding the bottle to your nose or through a diffuser, the plant essence reaches the olfactory system at the top of your nose. And activates your limbic system in the brain, telling it to start acting immediately. Our limbic system is the control center for emotions, mood, memory, motivation, pain center, and pleasure center within the body. Each oil contains different properties that trigger the brain to send unique healing messages to the correlating area of the body.

## Absorption Method

Another way to use essential oils is to apply them directly on the skin. The healing properties in oils are absorbed by our pores and hair follicles and move into the bloodstream. The bloodstream carries the chemical through its pathways and into the organs and body systems that they heal.

The best places to apply essential oils are to the bottoms of the feet, or the pulse points on the body, such as the temples, the back of the neck, or the inside of the wrists.

Important Note: ALWAYS dilute essential oils in a carrier oil before applying them to your skin! Remember, essential oils are highly concentrated, and some oils can burn the skin or cause skin irritation if applied directly to the skin. A good carrier oil would be coconut oil, almond oil, or olive oil.

One way I began using the essential oils was to change negative thought patterns, outdated beliefs, and negative emotions. This Aromatic Anchoring Technique is powerful and helped me to shift my mood so I could create a more positive state of wellbeing for my healing process.

## Anchoring High Vibe Thoughts

When we're creating a high vibe life, we need to replace many of the negative thoughts we have throughout the day with positive messaging. The inhalation method works well to help with creating new and powerful thoughts and beliefs. I found this technique to be quite powerful in changing my mindset and to produce a greater sense of wellbeing. It combines the power of scent with the power of visualization to create lasting change in our lives.

Here are some examples of essential oils and the energetic vibration and benefits they give to the body and mood centers.

- Citrus Oil (lemon, orange or lime)—helps connect with joy and happiness, renewal
- Lavender Oil—relaxation, release of stress, quiets a busy mind, cleansing
- Peppermint Oil—Refreshes the mind, better focus and awareness, increases energy
- Rose Oil—Opening the heart, love, protection, and enhances intuition

Aromatic anchoring is a technique we can use to manage our state of mind, change an unwanted thought, or an outdated belief.

1. Choose a time you won't be disturbed. Doing this technique in the morning will help set the tone for your day ahead, where doing it in the evening sets the tone for your subconscious mind while you sleep.
2. Choose an essential oil that resonates with you or one that vibrates with the emotion you're wanting to shift. Let your intuition guide you to the best oil for you.
3. Spend a couple of minutes doing some deep breaths and grounding yourself into the moment.
4. Bring the unwanted thought or belief that you desire to remove into your consciousness. Imagine the energy of this thought draining down from the top of your head, through each part of your body, out of each cell of your body, through the bottoms of your feet and into Mother Earth. Watch until it completely clears from your body.
5. Next, visualize the new empowering thought as it begins to flow through the top of your head, down into your body, into every cell, your arms, torso, legs, and feet. Fill yourself entirely with the new thought. Use your senses to see the thought, image, or affirmation. Feel it into every part of your body.
6. While visualizing the new thought, take the essential oil you chose, place a drop in the palm of your hand, and rub your hands together. Now cup your hands over your nose and breathe deeply while saying, feeling, and visualizing your new empowering thought out loud.
7. Drop your hands and move your arms to shake off the energy.
8. Repeat this process several times to strongly anchor the new thought. You are creating new neuro-pathways in the brain with this process.
9. Take a few deep cleansing breaths and thank your body for all that it does for you.

Anchoring can also be done throughout the day and in the moment of a negative thought, emotion, or experience. When you notice an unwanted thought, grab your bottle of essential oil, visualize a new empowering thought and breathe deeply from your bottle of essential oil. Soon you will be able to shift the negative response just by smelling the oil.

We can use the powerful sense of smell in our healing practice. Essential oils are powerful natural medicines gifted to us from Mother Nature. Essential oils contain the powerful essence of the plants that vibrate high to deepen our healing and spiritual practices. Use this powerful tool in your wellness routine and watch the healing power of nature elevate you.

---

**Bonnie Chase, RN, is the founder of Wild Woman Nation. She's a Holistic RN, Women's Wellness Coach, and Self-Care Advocate. She's a Conformity Slayer, Truth Seeker, and Free-Spirited Introvert.**

**Her Mission? Simply helping women tap into their intuition and listen to their bodies to create a healthy and happy life! She shows women how to break free from conformity, find their own voice, and speak their truth.**

**Her current home is in the Wild Heart of Oregon Wine Country with her charming hubby and 2 adorable poochies, Bill and Ted. Get Bonnie's free resources for healing your body and your life at http://bonniechase.com/book-resources**

# CHAPTER 23
# Guided Art Therapy
## The Clay Meditation Ball

BY BARBARA M. BUSTARD

## My Story

When I was two and a half years old, I was adopted. The story I was told by my adoptive mother went as so. My biological mother was a first cousin once removed to my adoptive mother. In other words, my biological mother was the daughter of my adoptive mother's first cousin. My biological parents were getting divorced, and my adoptive mother offered to "help with the girls (my sister and me) in any way." One day my biological mother called and said: "you can have them." According to my adoptive mother, when she went to pick us up, my biological mother just handed us over and waved goodbye! I have always struggled with the knowledge that I was so disposable that my own mother would just give me away so easily. This was especially so after I became a mother myself. When my two sons were close in age to the ages of my sister and me when we were given away, looking at them, I could not imagine just handing them over to someone else.

My childhood looked ideal to the outside world, but my adoptive mother was not at all nurturing or maternal. Quite the opposite, in fact. She was physically, verbally, and emotionally abusive. I often wondered why God would allow children to be given to someone who clearly did not want children. My consolation would be to tell myself that my current situation must be better than it would have been.

From childhood, I had an artist's spirit. I wrote poems. I carved a horse head in a discarded block of wood using a screwdriver and hammer. I always drew the picture in the back of magazines to see if I would be accepted for mail order drawing lessons. I painted ceramics at the local shop. I have a vivid memory of one day in elementary school that lit a spark in me. I think it was a summer program, and the teacher showed me a potter's wheel. It was in a little alcove in the teachers office. The moment I saw that potter's wheel and learned what could be created with it began my yearning to work in clay. That memory stayed with me for many years. It wasn't until my 30s, my yearning desire to learn the art of working in clay was realized.

My youngest son was attending preschool at the community college, and I decided to complete my AA degree, which I had aborted years ago. The only credits needed to complete the degree were electives. Looking through the course offerings, I noticed ceramics classes listed. I was surprised to see that you could earn credits for painting those little ceramic figurines that were so popular when I was a kid. Reading the course description, though, I discovered that ceramics was the art of clay: hand building, throwing on the potter's wheel, and sculpture. I took every class I could. I was in love with working in clay. Clay became my therapy. It was how I could feed my soul, relax, release anger and express my true self. For 20 plus years I was a potter and ceramic artist. Often, I felt a deep spiritual connection with the clay. It was as if Spirit was creating through me, using my hands to form the clay. Isaiah 64: 8 resonated through my being. "Yet, oh Lord, you are our Creator, we are the clay, and you are our potter. We are the work of your hand." So, it was no surprise when clay was the means for me to bring into form a major revelation.

One day when I was about 40, doing breathwork in yoga class, the teacher related that when done correctly, this breath would sound like being in your mother's womb. When she made this comment, my immediate thought was, *how would I know what that sounds like? I was never there!* Now of course I realized intellectually that I existed prior to my adoption, but that part of my life was a total blank. The fact that I'd never seen a picture of myself before the age of 2 1/2 combined with the childhood memory of my "mother" yelling, "Thank God you're none of my blood and never will be," had created a total disconnect to anyone having given birth to me. Several years later my life was on a different path. I was in the process of discernment for ordination and was in Spiritual Direction. When I conveyed this story to my spiritual director, she was not pleased at all with my lack of connection and informed me that I did not accept that I was a child of God. Driving home from our meeting I was furious!

How dare she say that to me! Then out of nowhere, I'm reciting Psalm 139:12,14,15. The strange part was that I was not a bible scholar! I did not really know the Psalms numbers or verse and was not able to recite them from memory. Nevertheless, I heard it as clear as day: *For you, yourself created my inmost parts. You knit me together in my mother's womb. My body was not hidden from you while I was being made in secret and woven in the depths of the earth. Your eyes beheld my limbs yet unfinished in the womb.* I was ecstatic! I got it! It didn't matter the people involved, or the secrets kept. God had been working this clay from the start. It was God that created me and was with me even if I had no memory or proof of my being. This clay was formed in God's womb, and that is where the journey began. Having come to this revelation, I knew I had to create something to commemorate it. As soon as I got home, I went to the studio and created a hollow ball of clay on which I engraved the words of Psalm 139. That ball is a constant reminder that I am somebody's child. I have made many meditation balls since that first one, some for inspiration, some for grief, inscribed with the names of loved ones, and others for joy and celebration. Each one has been a powerful healing tool, through the meditative creation process as well as holding it, reading it and feeling its weight in my hands for prayer or meditation.

Now it's time to guide you in creating your own meditation ball.

## The Tool

You will need:
1-2 lbs of air-dry clay (available at craft stores or online)
A small dish of water
A small dish of vinegar
A toothbrush
A toothpick
Alphabet rubber stamps or pencil with a rounded point
A small dish of corn starch
Parchment or waxed paper for your work surface

## The Process

You will begin with a meditation and move directly to creating the first pinch pot as a part of the meditation. Read through the entire exercise once to understand how to make a pinch pot and then begin.

Before beginning to meditate form two balls of clay using ½ to 1 lb. of clay for each ball. Form a rough ball in your hands, then roll it around on the table with the palm of your hand until you have a fairly round ball. (Note, remove your rings before you begin!)

Sit comfortably in a chair with your feet flat on the floor. Holding a ball of clay in your hands, place your hands in your lap. Keep your hands still in your and just let the clay sit in your hands.

Close your eyes and take three deep, cleansing breaths. Focus your mind's eye on the soles of your feet. Feel the floor supporting your feet. Release any tension you feel. Slowly, take time to check in with every part of your body, acknowledging any sensations you are feeling and releasing any tension being held. Move from your feet, to your ankles, lower legs, thighs, buttocks, stomach, lower back, chest, neck, back of your head, top of your head, your forehead, eyes, nose, mouth, down to your shoulders, your upper arms, and your forearms. Without moving them, focus on your hands and your fingers, and then notice the sensation of the clay in your hands. Notice its weight, its temperature, and it's texture. With your inner eye, stay focused on the clay and make an intention, prayer, or desire that you want the clay to hold.

Now, with your eyes remaining closed, hold your clay in your non-dominant hand and using your thumb from your dominant hand, push it into the center of the ball, stopping about a half-inch from the bottom. Be careful not to push all the way through your clay.

Squeezing gently with your thumb inside and your fingers on the outside, rotate and squeeze continuously around the opening until you have a bowl form. Be careful to leave the wall of your bowl at least ½ in thick. When you are satisfied with your pinch pot, and you are ready, slowly open your eyes.

Make your second pinch pot, keeping the size and thickness as close as possible to your first one. Check that the edges of your pots match up when placed on top of each other.

Dip your toothbrush in the vinegar and scrub the lip of each pot. Place the pinch pots on top of each other and using your finger, move clay from one pot to the other to seal the connection. This is not smooth and pretty. Make sure to join clay from each pot to the other.

Cupping the ball in your hands, pat it, and roll it until it is round. Place it on the table and roll it with the palm of your hand until you have a fairly smooth round shape. If it has small cracks and rough areas, dip your fingertip in water to smooth them. If it continues to crack slightly, poke a small hole with a toothpick to release some of the air inside.

Set your ball aside on the parchment or wax paper until it is firm but not dry. If you are leaving it overnight, cover it with a piece of plastic so that it does not get too dry.

Using either alphabet stamps or a pencil, or both, inscribe your ball with whatever is meaningful for you. Carve designs with a pencil if you wish. When using stamps, dip the stamp in corn starch then tap off the excess before pressing in the clay. This will keep it from sticking. Smooth any sharp edges from carving by dipping your fingertip in the water and gently rubbing the edges.

When your completed ball is dry, which could take as long as a week depending on the humidity, add color if you wish, using acrylic paint.

May this ball you have created be a reminder to you of your divine nature. Namaste.

---

**Barbara Bustard is a teaching artist providing private lessons as well as PaintNights and art parties for all ages, from preschoolers to seniors. For 20 years, she owned and operated her ceramics studio and The Footed Bowl gallery. A graduate of Notre Dame University of Maryland with a degree in Religious Studies and Art, Barbara particularly enjoys providing spiritual and meditative art experiences. She is a firm believer in the research, which shows that the mere act of creating something, regardless of the perfection of the end result, is very beneficial to one's mental, physical, and emotional health. Barbara strives to develop her students' creative potential, but most of all, a desire to create for the sake of creating. You can like and follow her at https://www.facebook.com/healingartforthesoul/ For an instructional video of the meditation go to https://youtu.be/lmFBBLQfE9I**

CHAPTER 24

# Energy Healing

## Clearing Ancestral Energy for Pain Free Living

BY JACQUELINE M. KANE

When our life is dysfunctional, we always seem to think, *everything's fine...it's great.* I know that's what I thought. By late 2009, I was building my business, working a full-time schedule, taking care of our two boys, going to the gym three to four times each week, we were socializing a lot, and I was meditating—mostly regularly. Overall, I told people I was feeling "okay." What I didn't understand was how depression had seeped into my life—or how my life was about to take a nose-dive and become gossip fodder.

But how did I get there?

It will help you to look at how my history was built on a rocky life-foundation—and what it took for me to rebuild it into something solid.

I grew up in a house my grandfather built—in Connecticut, USA. He was an Italian mason. He and my grandmother had endured a lot in Italy, including a war. They brought their family to America in 1956 when my mother was 14 years old. They arrived on the last successful voyage of the S.S. Andrea Doria. Due to the various hardships they'd been through, a great deal of fear had developed in the family. My mother became hardened.

Fast forward to the first jagged layers in my rickety beginnings. My family was headed by an emotionally-absent, Italian immigrant mother, and a silent, gear-head, farm-boy of a father. They both had vastly different ideas on how to raise a family than how most Americans "do" families today. There was no real thinking involved in the process. Coming from their own messy family histories, they simply reacted to their current circumstances. Manipulation, drama, yelling, and lies were the operating standard. It was also a closed-hearted setting. There were plenty of secrets. It was about survival and validating themselves. It didn't make for a loving or supportive environment.

My brother was the oldest child—and in an Italian family, that made him kind of like...God. My sister was born a year later, and she made damned sure everyone knew she was there. I was the third born out of four children—born into chaos and dysfunction. I quickly guessed that being the "good little girl" might be the safest way to get my needs met, and the attention I craved.

You might ask, "How did that work for you?" It turns out—not so great. It wasn't long before I learned my needs would never be met, and I had to become self-sufficient. Since my older siblings demanded so much attention, I faded into the background—I was usually minimalized and ignored. It became hard for me to ask for anything—they didn't listen anyway, and sometimes it only brought a barrage of loud, angry words in my direction. My attitude grew into, *What's the use? I'll never get what I want or need. So why bother?* I became silent. This was how I learned to be in the world.

It took me decades to realize that forcing myself into the "good little girl" role was not the way to happiness or love. I had created a life for myself that was all about making sure everyone else's needs were met, while I felt alone and trapped inside—even invisible. But at the time, I couldn't see this.

Along the way, the only people I could initially relate to or trust were my grandmother and a few teachers. It's probably the reason I became an outstanding student—I'd found my validation at school. I loved it, and it was the place I preferred to be the most. I put a lot of effort into making friends, and they became my support as well.

When deciding what to do after high school, it made sense to follow in my aunt's footsteps and entered a two-and-a-half-year program earning my Associate Degree in radiologic technology.

A few of us went on a "Singles Cruise" in 1987 to the Caribbean. We had a blast. While on the cruise, I experienced my first massage, ever. Oh...My...Word! It was amazing. After the massage, I felt incredibly relaxed and tranquil. I was suddenly aware of something missing—all of my mind-chatter had quieted. For the first time in my life, I was in a magnificent space of being present. No judgments. No worries. Just present and feeling the freedom to be me and feel at peace.

I thought, "*Wow. I want to do this someday—this work. I want to help other people feel like this.*" I was so mellow that afternoon, my girlfriends had to dress me and put on my makeup, so we could go out that evening.

And throughout all of this, I had a couple car accidents, which caused pain in my body.

I married my husband in 1992 and gradually, my earlier family pattern of trying to be "the good little girl" reemerged—only this time, I tried to be "the perfect wife." Somehow, it didn't occur to me that I needed to speak up and ask for what I wanted or needed. I guess I figured if he really loved me, he would simply *know*.

Healthy communication had never been modeled to me as a kid. I had no idea how to communicate effectively in a relationship. Consequently, I continued my old patterns of keeping quiet, not asking for help or what I needed, feeling unvalued, invisible, and the resulting resentment came pouring in.

By November 1999, my husband and I agreed I'd be attending Massage School. By then, we had 2 young boys, and needless to say, my life became hectic and overwhelming. I worked my job all day and did the wife-mom thing all evening. It felt like a 24/7, 365-day gig. There was no time off. I gradually began experiencing the physical effects of the car accidents, and the overwhelm of my life.

By the time December 2009 rolled around, my marriage and our relationship had become quite challenging. It was then that I made a decision that something had to change.

It was at that time that I had met Margaret Lynch and Alan Davidson, which catapulted me into deep healing. I had experienced an ancestral energy clearing and had this amazing breakthrough. I began to see myself in new ways. So many things started to shift inside of me. I found myself feeling less and less fear and anxiety. I started noticing people were noticing me more and were engaging more with me.

During that clearing, I discovered that so much of the fear and limitations I'd felt for most of my life were inherited from my parents and their ancestors. It was at that time that I began asking more questions about what life was like for my mother and my grandmother.

My mother grew up during WWll. My grandfather was a soldier fighting at the front lines while my grandmother was home alone, raising three children. Living in fear and worrying about his life, struggling to feed her family and living in constant fear of the German soldiers who'd invaded her town. It became very evident to me that my mother was carrying a high level of fear in her physical system and that it was passed down to me.

We are all energetic beings susceptible to the energy of others. It starts in the womb. For nine months, we are exposed to the hormones, nutrition, and emotional state of our mother and take on her energy. We are conceived inside of her.

All of her worries, concerns, joys, and excitement surround us. And that's where our ancestral energy begins because our mom was carrying her mother's energy, beliefs, and programming. Along with our fathers. There were even ancestral health conditions, pain, and suffering entering into us in the womb. It becomes our DNA, our cells are created in that energy, it becomes our nervous system, and every system in our body is created from that energy. The DNA of your personal family trauma is being passed down from generation to generation.

Along with our parent's energy, we also inherited our parents' ancestor's unresolved emotional issues, problems, and trauma. These patterns can have an inhibiting or disruptive influence on your life today. Some of these can create obstacles in your lives, blocking your pathway to joy, abundance, authentic power, and unlimited possibilities.

You may be hearing the word ancestral energy for the first time today, but this is why you need to pay attention now. Trauma is energy, and energy is us. The energy of your trauma is stored in your physical body. To heal our physical body, we have to address the trauma stored in the body.

Scientists are now studying how the grandchildren of the Holocaust victims are impacted by ancestral energy leading to grief, sadness, or pain. It's been written that they experience guilt around being alive. That guilt will then show up in every area of their lives. They can feel bad about being successful and doing well. They could experience a lot of sadness in their lives and not understand why. You can read more here about the story: https://www.theguardian.com/science/2015/aug/21/study-of-holocaust-survivors-finds-trauma-passed-on-to-childrens-genes

For me, I remember growing up with fear and worry and not really knowing why I was always nervous. That worry and fear kept me exhausted and depressed for years. That was when I was diagnosed with Chronic Fatigue Syndrome and was living with physical pain in my hips and low back.

Some families have a family history of allergies or heart conditions. These conditions become the truth of the family. You can hear members saying, "Yes, heart attacks run in my family. It's just the way it is." It becomes the truth of the family, an imprinted belief.

Here are some signs and symptoms of Ancestral Wounds:

Heart conditions
Anxiety
Depression

Patterns of feeling unfulfilled
Arthritis
Headaches

If you experience any of these symptoms, then ancestral healing may be the missing link that can help you live pain-free and personally fulfilled.

When we clear the energy, then you have the opportunity to choose a new way of being. Your body and mind can then begin to choose how you want to feel. You can choose what new beliefs you want to believe about yourself.

When that change occurs, physical healing can be achieved faster and easier. You can get back to living your life with more ease and flow. You have new awareness around your pain and can feel empowered around your health and life.

Ancestral clearing has made a huge difference in my life. I no longer worry about things. I get to choose to trust in myself and that I am fully supported in all areas of my life. This has all resulted in allowing more ease and flow into my marriage, enjoying fun, adventurous vacations, a successful business, and being more present when hanging out with friends.

There are 5 main areas where ancestral energy patterns have an impact:

1. Physical pain
2. Conflict in your relationships
3. Cash flow: money with meaning
4. Spiritual connections
5. Accessing your true authentic self and your leadership potential

Standing in your power is succeeding in all 5 of these areas. The price of not healing this ancestral energy is not standing in your power, crippling self-doubt, confusion, lack of clarity, lack of action towards your soul's purpose, and your sacred calling

Let's clear this so that you can achieve your goals faster and easier.

You could also think of recording this so that later on, you can have this on your own. If you'd like to listen to an audio version of what's written below, along with journaling questions, go to my resource page: https://jacquelinemkane.com/resources.

## The Process:

- Setup: First, sit in a chair and relax. Turn off all distractions. Take a deep breath and bring that oxygen all the way down your entire body and into your toes. Take three of these deep body breaths.

Repeat this phrase: I, (and state your name), bring back my energy from all the places I've left it. Repeat this 3 times. Over time you should be able to feel your energy coming back to you like a warm blanket.

- Discovery: Focus on your physical or emotional pain. When you think of this pain, how does it make you feel? What is the emotion that comes up when you think of this pain? Most people say it's frustration or annoyance. Whatever it is focus on that emotion.

- Visualize: Use your imagination to see where this emotion and energy is stored in your body. Now use your visualization to scoop this energy and emotion and bring it outside of your body. Scoop up as much of it as you can and bring it outside of you into a ball in front of your heart.

- Send it back: Now see your parents standing in front of you. Say to them, "This was never mine to carry, it's time to hand this back." Then see yourself handing this energetic ball back to them.

See them taking back this ball of energy, and now they are saying to you, "I never wanted my child to carry this, it's time to hand this back." Visualize your parents taking it back. Now see their parents standing in front of your parents and see them having the same conversation. See them taking back this ball of energy. See each generation stepping in to pass back this ball of energy. Going back through time from one generation to the next all the way to when it was first created. It's okay if you don't see that, you may feel it or have a knowing that it's at the very beginning.

- Transform: Now visualize golden liquid light coming down from the heavens and transmuting that energy into its complete polar opposite. Bring this new energy of hope, love, abundance, and freedom down as it passes through each one of those ancestors. Passing through there head, down through there body, as it invigorates every cell in their body with this new energy. See it passing from one generation to the next, lighting up each one of them.

Bring this new energy all the way down to you. Allow this new energy to flow through your head and all the way to your toes. Feel this new vibrant energy as it lights you up.

- Ground: Now bring this new energy out your toes and deep into the earth. Ground this new energy of who you are down through the layers of the planet and secure it into the earth. Really feel this new energy of love and ease into your body and into your life. Take a few minutes here and breathe this in.

Breathe into this new you.

Take another deep breath and slowly come back into your body and back to the here and now.

Feel free to take a few minutes to write down what this experience was like for you.

Also, go to my resource page for more journaling prompts.

Feel free to contact me at jacqueline@jacquelinemkane.com and share what it was like for you.

From my heart to yours, I send you love and healing and wish you a life filled with abundance in all areas.

---

**By diving deep underneath the surface and symptoms of chronic pain, Jacqueline Kane, the Stop the Pain Specialist, supports women in discovering and healing the crucial hidden links between physical pain, finances, and the ability to live a full life. With over 15-years in private practice as a healer and over 30-years in health care, Jacqueline has merged her innate wisdom with a multitude of healing modalities, including Bowenwork, Massage Therapy, Emotional Freedom Technique, Evolutionary Meditation, Soul Clearing, Tapping into Wealth, Past Lives Regression, Ancestral Clearing, and more to create unique, results-oriented methods for healing.**

**Jacqueline's powerful programs, available to individuals, groups, and organizations, liberate clients from both physical pain and financial struggle, so they create a path to energy, health, ease with money, and personal fulfillment. She is the creator of the *Healthy Wealthy Success System©* that guides women in creating a joyful, pain-free life full of energy and financial success. Learn more at www.JacquelineKane.com**

## CHAPTER 25

# When to Hire a Guide

## Take Your Health and Wellness to the Next Level

### BY LAURA DI FRANCO, MPT

All the experts here agree that empowering you by giving you tools to treat yourself at home is one of the keys to healing. When you take responsibility for self-awareness, self-care, self-healing, and self-development, you are much more apt to feel good and stay feeling that way. We've experienced clients who take self-treatment to heart getting better faster, staying healthier in the long run, and really enjoying their lives to the fullest.

We also know many people need skilled assistance and guidance to feel better. The clients we come across are in all stages of physical, mental, and emotional dis-ease or dysfunction. Some need a quick tool and home program, while others require intensive or prolonged care. We all agree that having a guide on the journey is paramount to peak performance, whatever stage you're in.

When you have a guide, coach, or healer in your corner, you'll reach your goals faster, but more importantly, you'll have someone invested in your progress and healing, and you won't be doing it alone. Remember, that guide has been where you are, and has healed the layers you're going through. He or she is able to hold a healing space for you to do that same work. Holding a healing space for you means they've practiced a conscious presence, an ability to ground and center themselves, and an ability to energetically enhance your healing process. That conscious presence is not something you find in all people. It's a practice that healers have worked for years to master. They've adopted a lifestyle that includes these skills and tools, so they can help others. They are special, amazing people.

This final note is to encourage you to seek out a guide if you feel like you're stuck, not making progress, feeling more hopeless than hopeful, or just can't consistently get your mindset to stay positive, open, or clear. We encourage you to explore different modalities and different guides, coaches, and practitioners. Find someone you vibe with and hire them to help you get to where you want to go.

Try asking: What else is possible for my healing today? Just asking yourself that question should help you feel hopeful. Sit with that question without straining to hear an answer. Allow yourself to meditate on the possibility.

Another great question to sit with, and/or journal about: What if there's something you haven't learned yet that could change everything?

We sit around and think we've read it all, done it all, and learned it all, and we stay resigned to our current mediocre physical, mental, emotional status because we think there are no alternatives or options left. I've been exploring healing and the vast array of healing modalities for an entire lifetime, and I'm here to tell you I won't have time to get to all the possibilities.

The point here is there are people out there who will help you heal. There's a guide out there waiting to teach you something you didn't even know existed and expose you to another level of hope you didn't realize you could feel. This book outlines dozens of those approaches. Some traditional. Some alternative. Some you may have never heard of. Some you may have heard of but never tried. It's time to explore!

It's our job as authentic healers, practitioners, and guides to facilitate a process of healing in you, connect you with your inner healer and power, and super-boost that power inside you. And we're good at it. Try us!

Please go back to the chapters that drew you in, piqued your interest, or had you feeling a little excited. Look up the amazing author there and read a little bit more about them on their website. You might even contact them to say thank you for their words, or set up a call with them to discuss what you learned. The authors I asked to be a part of this are cool like that; they want you to feel better, and they are open-hearted, skilled, and very aware and experienced healers. They thrive when you thrive. It's part of their mission, like it is mine, to help heal the world.

I hope you enjoyed this book. Even more than that, I hope you're getting into action with it, trying the exercises and tools, and getting some results! I'd love to hear how you're doing. Hop over to www.BraveHealer.com and send me a note!

Lastly, I have a personal favor to ask. If you enjoyed this book and have a couple minutes to leave a review on Amazon, I'd greatly appreciate it. Your review helps others see our book, and it spreads the good vibes. Thank you!

Signing off now with a final wish for your best health. May you find what you need to thrive, mind, body, and soul.

With warrior love,<br>
Laura

# A Rampage of Gratitude

Gratitude is the energy I want to purposefully end the book with, in hopes you'll read this last page and imagine all the people in your own life you're grateful for, maybe even some of these fantastic authors!

This is more than acknowledging people for their help with this book, it's conjuring up energy we can take with us as we move forward into our purpose and mission of helping the world heal. Appreciation is the energy of manifestation! It's a magical, foundational mindset that everything good is born from.

So, amazing reader, thank you for being here! For being open to learning. And for exploring this fascinating world of healing with me and all of the authors here. You are powerful, and have limitless potential to heal yourself! Step into your power, use the tools, ask more questions, and adopt a lifestyle of learning. That's how you'll continue to evolve and feel the most peace, happiness, and health in the future. I'm so grateful to be walking alongside you on this journey.

To my authors, the badassery you've laid down on these pages is beyond what I'd hoped for. In the many conversations I had with you during the writing phase of your chapters you gave me your trust, and allowed me to inspire you, even though you may have been unsure. You believed me when I told you how important your authentic stories are and you told them, without apology, and with a stupendous courage and generosity. Thank you for that. Thank you for saying yes (all 24 of you in 48 hours!). And thank you for stepping up to teach what you know and gift our readers with your unique expertise, knowledge and skills. I'm so frickin honored to be in your company.

To our book designer, Christy Collins, thank you for stepping up to make this book shine. I feel super grateful to know you and to have found someone who really understands my Brave Healing message.

To all our friends, family, colleagues, acquaintances and book launch team members who supported us during the writing, publishing, launching and promoting of this project, thank you so much for your support, love, words of encouragement, and purchases. This village is badass!

# Other Books by Laura Di Franco

*Living, Healing and Tae Kwon Do, a Memoir to Inspire Your Inner Warrior*

*Brave Healing, a Guide for Your Journey*

*Your High Vibe Business, a Strategic Workbook for Badass Entrepreneurial Success*

*Warrior Love, a Journal to Inspire Your Fiercely Alive Whole Self*

*Warrior Joy, a Journal to Inspire Your Fiercely Alive Whole Self*

*Warrior Soul, a Journal to Inspire Your Fiercely Alive Whole Self*

*Warrior Dreams, a Journal to Inspire Your Fiercely Alive Whole Self*

*Warrior Desire, Love Poems to Inspire Your Fiercely Alive Whole Self*

Your words will change the world when you're brave enough to share them. Your fear of not-good-enough is boring. What if the thing you're still a little afraid to share is exactly what someone needs to hear to change, or even save their life? It's time to be brave.

–Laura Di Franco

Made in USA - Kendallville, IN
1115368_9781733073882
05.26.2020 0817